MW01073962

THE
ULTIMATE
MARVEL STUDIOS
QUIZ BOOK

First published in the UK in 2022 by Studio Press,
an imprint of Bonnier Books UK,
4th Floor, Victoria House, Bloomsbury Square, London, WC1B 4DA
Owned by Bonnier Books,
Sveavägen 56, Stockholm, Sweden

bonnierbooks.co.uk

1 3 5 7 9 10 8 6 4 2

All rights reserved
ISBN 978-1-80078-337-9

Additional questions written by Susie Rae
Translated by Laura Pollard
Edited by Frankie Jones
Designed by Maddox Philpot
Production by Emma Kidd

A CIP catalogue record for this book is available from the British Library
Printed and bound in Great Britain by Clays Ltd, Elcograf S.p.A.

THE
ULTIMATE
MARVEL STUDIOS
QUIZ BOOK

OVER 1,000 QUESTIONS TO TEST
YOUR SUPER HERO KNOWLEDGE!

STUDIO
PRESS

CONTENTS

INTRODUCTION

When it comes to the Marvel Cinematic Universe, are you a pro who knows everything there is to know about this iconic brand? Or are you not sure which archnemesis belongs to which Super Hero, and couldn't name a single Avenger? Well, no matter your level of Marvel knowledge, this is the book for you! Inside these pages, you'll find over 1,000 questions about everything MCU. From *Iron Man* to *Eternals* and everything in-between, there are over 30 movies and streaming series to test your knowledge on.

To make sure there is something for everyone, each quiz has three levels ranked by difficulty:

◢□□ New Fan (easy)
◢◢□ Casual Fan (medium)
◢◢◢ Super Fan (difficult)

If you're a bit unsure about your Marvel facts, start off with the New Fan questions for that quiz. The Casual Fan questions are best suited to those with a decent amount of Marvel knowledge. And if you think you're up for the ultimate challenge, test your skills with the Super Fan questions!

So, get ready to challenge yourself, your friends and your family to find out who will be crowned champion of the Ultimate Marvel Studios Quiz!

Turn to the back of the book for the answers.

IRON MAN

1. At the start of the movie, Tony is presenting his latest creation. What is it?
a The Jericho Missile
b The Antioch Assassin
c The Babylon Bomb

2. In which country is Tony taken hostage at the start of *Iron Man*?
a Sokovia
b Afghanistan
c Cuba

3. What is the name of the professor who grafts an electromagnet to Tony?
a Dr. Ho Yinsen
b Dr. Mo Harold
c Dr. Jack MacLennan

4. What colour is Iron Man's first armour?
a Blue
b Green
c Grey

5. Who plunges their hand into Tony's chest to help him install his palladium generator?
a Obadiah Stane
b James 'Rhodey' Rhodes
c Pepper Potts

6. When does Tony Stark say these words: 'Sometimes you gotta run before you can walk'?

  a After he escapes capture

  b Before his first flight in the new Iron Man armour

  c Before he kisses Pepper Potts

7. What is the name of the armour worn by Obadiah Stane?

  a Iron Monger

  b Iron Shield

  c Iron Crusher

8. Where is Tony's villa located?

  a In New York City

  b In Malibu, California

  c In Afghanistan

9. What is the name of Tony Stark's AI?

  a JARVIS

  b ANDREW

  c GARRETT

10. How old was Tony when he became CEO of Stark Industries?
- **a** 21
- **b** 30
- **c** 45

11. Which lieutenant colonel of the US Air Force is also Tony's best friend?
- **a** George 'Johnny' Johnson
- **b** James 'Rhodey' Rhodes
- **c** James 'Bucky' Buchanan Barnes

12. Who betrays Tony?
- **a** Obadiah Stane
- **b** James 'Rhodey' Rhodes
- **c** Pepper Potts

13. 'You've been called the da Vinci of our time'. How does Tony respond to this statement by Christine Everhart?
- **a** 'Absolutely ridiculous. I don't paint.'
- **b** 'I think of myself more like van Gogh.'
- **c** 'Who's da Vinci?'

14. By which name do we better know Harold Joseph Hogan?
a   Sleepy Hogan
b   Grumpy Hogan
c   Happy Hogan

15. Without his arc reactor, what happens to Tony?
a   He falls asleep
b   His heart stops
c   He gains super-strength

16. Which S.H.I.E.L.D. agent appears for the first time in *Iron Man*?
a   Phil Coulson
b   Hawkeye
c   Black Widow

17. True or false? Tony Stark's first red and gold armour is the MARK II.

18. During the press conference he gives on his return from Afghanistan, what decision does Tony announce?
a   To retire to Miami
b   To build more Iron Man suits
c   To close the weapons division of Stark International

19. What is the last line of the film (before the post-credits scene)?

a   'I am Iron Man.'

b   'I will form the Avengers.'

c   'What are you doing?'

20. Who does Tony meet in the film's post-credits scene?

a   Captain America

b   Nick Fury, Director of S.H.I.E.L.D.

c   Howard Stark, his father.

21. What does Nick Fury come to talk to Tony about in the post-credits scene?

a   Hulk going on a rampage

b   Having an Iron Man suit of his own

c   The Avengers Initiative

22. What is Christine Everhart's job?

a   Journalist

b   Spy

c   Doctor

23. What does Pepper have inscribed on Tony's first arc reactor?

a   'I AM IRON MAN'

b   'PROOF THAT YOU'RE STILL ALIVE'

c   'PROOF THAT TONY STARK HAS A HEART'

24. What powers the electromagnet that Dr. Yinsen put in Tony's chest?
a   A car battery
b   The sun
c   A nuclear cell

25. How does Tony escape from the desert?
a   He flies out in his suit
b   James 'Rhodey' Rhodes rescues him in a helicopter
c   He rides a camel to a nearby village

THE INCREDIBLE HULK

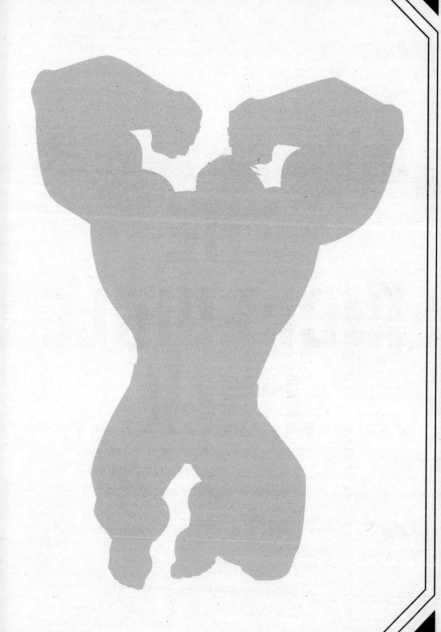

1. What kind of rays was Bruce Banner exposed to?

a   Methane rays

b   Gamma rays

c   Death rays

2. By what name do we better know Emil Blonsky?

a   Abomination

b   Ultron

c   Ebony Maw

3. What is Samuel Sterns' codename (the cellular biologist with whom Bruce corresponds)?

a   Mr. Red

b   Mr. Blue

c   Mr. Green

4. What is Bruce Banner's side job in Rio?

a   Janitor in a fireworks warehouse

b   Fry cook in a burger joint

c   Handyman in a bottling factory

5. Who chases Bruce Banner through the favelas of Rio?

a   The US army, led by General Ross

b   S.H.I.E.L.D., led by Nick Fury

c   The Brazilian police force

◢▱▱▱ **6.** 'Me in a metal tube, deep underground with hundreds of people in the most aggressive city in the world?' Who says this?
a   Emil Blonsky
b   Bruce Banner
c   Betty Ross

◢▱▱▱ **7.** What happens to Bruce Banner when he gets a little stressed?
a   He gains the ability to fly
b   He cries
c   He becomes the Incredible Hulk

◢◢◢▱ **8.** Where did Bruce Banner first change into Hulk after a laboratory accident in the opening of the film?
a   Culver University
b   AIM
c   Stark Industries

◢◢◢▱ **9.** What does Bruce Banner do just before he jumps out of the helicopter to confront Abomination?
a   He punches himself in the face
b   He kisses Betty
c   He screams

10. 'Let's rebalance the game.' Who says this?
  a   Emil Blonsky
  b   Bruce Banner
  c   Betty Ross

11. What provokes Bruce into turning into Hulk at Culver University?
  a   Betty breaking up with him
  b   A student laughing at him
  c   Tear gas being fired at him

12. Who is Betty Ross' father?
  a   Howard Stark, founder of Stark Industries
  b   General Ross, who is coordinating the hunt for Bruce
  c   Emil Blonsky

13. Which practice helps Bruce to control his heartbeat and manage his emotions?
  a   Jogging
  b   Meditation
  c   Yoga

14. What do two halves of a police car become when Hulk gets his hands on them?
  a   Boxing gloves
  b   Scrap metal
  c   A shield

15. At the start of *The Incredible Hulk*, how many days has it been since Bruce last transformed?
a 148
b 158
c 168

16. Who is Betty Ross' boyfriend when Bruce returns to the US?
a The psychiatrist Leonard Samson
b The dentist George Sandison
c The chiropodist Stephen Anderson

17. What is Betty Ross' job?
a Chemist
b Physicist
c Biologist

18. What does Emil Blonsky demand of Samuel Sterns?
a That he gives him the location of Bruce Banner
b That he sells him the formula that turned Bruce Banner into Hulk
c That he injects him with a sample of Bruce Banner's irradiated blood

19. What explosive cocktail creates Abomination?

a A mixture of Super Soldier Serum and synthetic gamma-irradiated blood from Bruce

b A mixture of Super Soldier Serum and dynamite

c A mixture of dynamite and synthetic gamma-irradiated blood from Bruce

20. How does Hulk extinguish a fire without having to move?

a He smothers it with his body

b He triggers a shock wave by clapping his hands

c He screams so loudly that his breath extinguishes it

21. Who does General Ross meet in a bar at the end of the film?

a Tony Stark

b Bruce Banner

c Nick Fury

22. What object becomes contaminated with Bruce Banner's blood?

a A slice of pizza

b A tin of dog food

c A bottle of soda

23. What is the name of Bruce's old friend's pizzeria?
a   Rio's
b   Stanley's
c   Antonio's

24. What dictionary does Bruce delve into at the start of the film?
a   An English-Portuguese dictionary
b   An English-Arabic dictionary
c   An English-Spanish dictionary

25. In Brazil, who informed Bruce that he was being tracked by Ross and his men?
a   His neighbour
b   His dog
c   His landlord

IRON MAN 2

1. What are the names of Tony's parents?
a   James and Olivia Stark
b   Peter and Jasmine Stark
c   Howard and Maria Stark

2. Which powerful Avenger appears in *Iron Man 2*?
a   Natasha Romanoff, aka Black Widow
b   Clint Barton, aka Hawkeye
c   Thor

3. Who first created Stark Expo?
a   Pepper Potts
b   Tony Stark
c   Howard Stark

4. Under what name does Natasha Romanoff join Stark Industries?
a   Nora Richardson
b   Natalie Rushman
c   Nicola Rogers

5. 'What is and always will be my greatest creation... is you.' Who says these words to whom?
a   Tony Stark to JARVIS
b   Pepper Potts to Tony
c   Howard Stark to his son, Tony

6. Who speaks, among other languages, English, French, Italian, Russian and Latin?
- **a** Pepper Potts
- **b** Tony Stark
- **c** Natalie Rushman (aka Natasha Romanoff, Black Widow)

7. Who finds Tony 'so predictable'?
- **a** Pepper Potts
- **b** Ivan Vanko, aka Whiplash
- **c** Natasha Romanoff, aka Black Widow

8. How does Natasha Romanoff describe Tony in her report for S.H.I.E.L.D.?
- **a** Controlling, arrogant and very loud
- **b** Compulsive, self-destructive and very narcissistic
- **c** Difficult to work with

9. Who is Tony Stark's new rival in *Iron Man 2*?
- **a** Justin Hammer
- **b** Obadiah Stane
- **c** Aldrich Killian

10. Whose codename is War Machine?
a Justin Hammer
b Ivan Vanko
c James 'Rhodey' Rhodes

11. Why is Tony on the brink of death?
a His palladium generator is slowly poisoning his blood
b His cholesterol is high
c His Iron Man suit is giving him lead poisoning

12. Who stops Tony when he loses it during his birthday party?
a Pepper Potts with the MARK I armour
b James 'Rhodey' Rhodes with the MARK II armour
c Nick Fury

13. What is Ivan Vanko's, aka Whiplash's, goal?
a To take over the world
b To destroy S.H.I.E.L.D.
c To avenge his father and bring down Tony

14. Who does Tony put in charge of Stark Industries in *Iron Man 2*?
a James 'Rhodey' Rhodes
b Natalie Rushman
c Pepper Potts

15. 'You're no longer Iron Man. You're just a drunk guy in a metal suit.' Who says these hurtful words to Tony?

a   James 'Rhodey' Rhodes
b   Justin Hammer
c   Pepper Potts

16. Who asks Natasha Romanoff to spy on Tony?

a   Agent Coulson of S.H.I.E.L.D.
b   Justin Hammer
c   Nick Fury, director of S.H.I.E.L.D.

17. What does Agent Coulson find in a crater in New Mexico in the post-credits scene?

a   The Tesseract
b   Mjolnir, Thor's hammer
c   Captain America's shield

18. What is Ivan Vanko's father's name?

a   Alexi
b   Konrad
c   Anton

19. What does Ivan Vanko, aka Whiplash, demand from Justin Hammer?
- **a** His bird
- **b** His own Iron Man suit
- **c** A powerful whip

20. Which senator tries to recover Iron Man's technology?
- **a** Senator Carlson
- **b** Senator Stern
- **c** Senator Goldsmith

21. How does Tony describe the Iron Man armour to the Senate Armed Services Committee?
- **a** A powerful weapon
- **b** A costume
- **c** A high-tech prosthesis

22. At which Grand Prix does Tony decide to compete?
- **a** Monaco
- **b** Miami
- **c** Australian

23. Why was Anton Vanko deported from the United States?
- **a** He killed Howard Stark
- **b** He was accused of espionage
- **c** He blew up a factory

24. What does Tony exchange his watch for?
- **a** A car
- **b** Strawberries
- **c** A ride on the bus

25. Who takes control of Hammer's drones?
- **a** Ivan Vanko
- **b** James 'Rhodey' Rhodes
- **c** Senator Stern

THOR

1. Who is the King of the Frost Giants of Jotunheim?
a   Odin
b   Loki
c   Laufey

2. What are the names of the Warriors Three who accompany Thor on his adventures?
a   Volstagg, Hogun and Fandral
b   Sif, Magnus and Freya
c   Heimdall, Freya and Hadurr

3. What does it take to be able to lift Thor's hammer?
a   Great strength
b   To be worthy
c   To be the true King of Asgard

4. What is the name of the rainbow bridge that connects Asgard to Midgard?
a   The Cosmic Gate
b   The Bifrost
c   Heimdall's Way

5. Which young Earth scientist falls in love with Thor?
a   Dr. Jane Foster
b   Darcy Lewis
c   Wanda Maximoff

▰▰▱ **6.** Which Asgard warrior is Thor's childhood friend?
a Loki
b Heimdall
c Sif

▰▱▱ **7.** Which Asgard warrior watches over the Bifrost?
a Fandral
b Heimdall
c Sif

▰▰▰ **8.** Which indestructible metal is Thor's hammer forged from?
a Vibranium
b Titanium
c Uru

▰▰▱ **9.** Which character kills his biological father in *Thor*?
a Loki
b Odin
c Thor

10. Which almost indestructible creature does Loki send to kill Thor?
- **a** The Obliterator
- **b** The Destroyer
- **c** Hela

11. Which eye is Odin missing?

12. Who does Dr. Erik Selvig mentor?
- **a** Dr. Jane Foster and her assistant, Darcy
- **b** Thor and his brother, Loki
- **c** Tony Stark

13. What is in the suitcase that Nick Fury opens in the post-credits scene?
- **a** Thor's hammer, Mjolnir
- **b** A nuclear weapon
- **c** The Tesseract

14. 'Well, I guess that's worth a look.' Who says these words after discovering the Tesseract? (Two possible answers)
- **a** Darcy Lewis
- **b** Loki
- **c** Dr. Jane Foster
- **d** Dr. Erik Selvig

15. Who is Frigga?
- **a** The mother of Thor and the Queen of Asgard
- **b** The mother of Loki and the wife of Laufey
- **c** The blacksmith who forged Mjolnir

16. Why can't Thor lift Mjolnir once he is on Earth?
- **a** Because gravity is different on Asgard
- **b** Because he was banished by Odin
- **c** Because he chose to give up his powers

17. What do Asgardians call Earth?
- **a** Midgard
- **b** Little Asgard
- **c** Terra

18. What happens to the Bifrost at the end of *Thor*?
- **a** It is opened to all humans
- **b** It is locked
- **c** It is destroyed

19. Which new Avenger appears in *Thor*?
- **a** Natasha Romanoff, aka Black Widow
- **b** Clint Barton, aka Hawkeye
- **c** Tony Stark, aka Iron Man

20. How does Thor become worthy of Mjolnir again?
a By sparing Loki's life
b By joining the Avengers
c By agreeing to sacrifice himself for Jane and her friends

21. What happens after Thor says 'How dare you attack the son of Odin!'?
a Darcy tasers him
b Jane punches him
c Thor passes out

22. When he asks Phil Coulson to release him, by which false identity does Erik Selvig claim to know him?
a Dr. David Evans
b Dr. Daniel McWilliam
c Dr. Donald Blake

23. Who rescues Thor and his companions from the clutches of the Frost Giants at the start of the film?
a Loki
b Odin
c Heimdall

24. Who decides to go to Earth to bring Thor back to Asgard?

a   Sif and the Warriors Three

b   Loki

c   Heimdall

25. How many hits are needed for the Destroyer to seriously injure Thor?

a   It can't injure him

b   Dozens

c   A single hit

CAPTAIN AMERICA: THE FIRST AVENGER

1. What part of New York is Steve Rogers from?

a Queens

b Brooklyn

c Manhattan

2. Which treasure of Odin did Hydra seize in Norway?

a The Tesseract

b Mjolnir

c His eyepatch

3. Who chooses Steve Rogers to be the first super soldier?

a Dr. Anderson

b Dr. Carter

c Dr. Erskine

4. How did Steve Rogers' father die?

a In a mustard gas attack

b From a heart attack

c From asthma

5. Name an object used by Steve Rogers as a shield before becoming Captain America. (Two possible answers)

a A table

b A park bench

c A taxi door

d A bin lid

6. What prototype does Howard Stark demonstrate at the World Exposition of Tomorrow?

a A flying car
b Iron Man armour
c A vibranium shield

7. How many times did Steve try to enlist?

a Three
b Five
c Seven

8. Which scientist does Red Skull fund the work of?

a Dr. Luther Fischer
b Dr. Anders McCoy
c Dr. Arnim Zola

9. What does Steve say, after the transformation, when Agent Carter asks him how he feels?

a 'Stronger'
b 'Taller'
c 'Invincible'

10. What is the main material in Captain America's shield?

a Titanium
b Steel
c Vibranium

11. During his transformation into a super soldier, Steve Rogers was exposed to which kind of radiation?

a Vita radiation

b Zola radiation

c Gamma radiation

12. What is the main property of vibranium?

a It is unbreakable

b It is lighter than air

c It absorbs vibrations

13. Colonel Chester Philips doesn't like Steve at first. Why does he change his mind?

a Steve risks his life to intercept a grenade

b Steve beats the other recruits in a race

c Steve charms Peggy Carter

14. By which name do we better know Johann Schmidt?

a Black Spine

b Red Skull

c Yellow Fibula

15. Who is Steve Rogers' best friend?

a John 'Jamie' Jamison

b Jack 'Robbie' Robertson

c James Buchanan 'Bucky' Barnes

16. When he wakes up at the end of the film, for how long has Captain America been asleep?

a   For nearly 50 years

b   For nearly 60 years

c   For nearly 70 years

17. What is the conversation about between Peggy and Steve before his plane crashes in the Arctic?

a   They plan to go out dancing

b   They talk about defeating Red Skull

c   They discuss their favourite foods

18. What does Red Skull owe his unique appearance to?

a   To being exposed to gamma radiation

b   To the side effects of the first iteration of Super Soldier Serum

c   To a skin condition

19. What happens to the Tesseract at the end of the film?

a   It disappears with Steve, deep in the Arctic

b   It is destroyed

c   It is stolen by Red Skull

20. Who says 'Cut off one head and two shall take its place. Hail Hydra!'?

a   Arnim Zola

b   Fred Clemson

c   Heinz Kruger

21. When Steve wakes up decades later, which environment did S.H.I.E.L.D. design to spare him from too much shock?

a His bedroom at home

b A simulated 1940s environment

c Peggy Carter's living room

22. How does Bucky Barnes disappear?

a He falls off a train

b His plane crashes into the ocean

c He drives a truck off a cliff

23. What is Jacques Dernier's area of expertise?

a Mechanical engineer

b Mathematician

c Explosives specialist

24. 'You have been asleep for nearly 70 years. You gonna be ok?'
'Yeah, it's just I had a date.'
Who has this exchange?

a Nick Fury and Steve Rogers

b Peggy Carter and Steve Rogers

c Arnim Zola and Bucky Barnes

25. When Steve gets his vibranium shield from Stark, who shoots him to test it?

a Bucky Barnes

b Peggy Carter

c Howard Stark

26. What kind of dance does Steve suggest to Peggy during their final exchange before his crash in the Arctic?
- **a** A foxtrot
- **b** A Charleston
- **c** A slow dance

27. Who is Dr. Erskine's assassin, sent by Red Skull?
- **a** Heinz Kruger
- **b** Arnim Zola .
- **c** Bucky Barnes

28. What is the nickname of Howling Commandos member Timothy Dugan?
- **a** Duggo
- **b** Dum Dum
- **c** Big Tim

29. Which senator hires Steve Rogers to play Captain America in a series of propaganda videos?
- **a** Senator Brandt
- **b** Senator Jones
- **c** Senator Williamson

30. What nationality is Howling Commandos member Jacques Dernier?
- **a** British
- **b** Italian
- **c** French

MARVEL'S THE AVENGERS

1. How many Avengers are there in the first instalment of their adventures? Bonus points if you can name them!

a   Five

b   Six

c   Seven

2. Which alien race does Loki ally himself with?

a   The Chitauri

b   The Frost Giants

c   The Skrull

3. Which eye is Nick Fury blind in?

a   His left eye

b   His right eye

4. Who attempts to stop Loki from escaping with Phil Coulson, Dr. Erik Selvig and the Tesseract from the S.H.I.E.L.D. Research Center?

a   Clint Barton, aka Hawkeye

b   Nick Fury

c   Maria Hill

5. Which initiative does Nick Fury restart in order to retrieve the Tesseract?

a   The Marvel Initiative

b   The Avengers Initiative

c   The Defenders Initiative

6. Who calls Natasha Romanoff in the middle of an interrogation?

a Nick Fury

b Clint Barton, aka Hawkeye

c Agent Phil Coulson

7. Who goes to India to convince Bruce Banner to rejoin the Avengers?

a Natasha Romanoff, aka Black Widow

b Nick Fury

c Tony Stark, aka Iron Man

8. What do we learn about Phil Coulson's girlfriend at the top of Stark Tower?

a She is Italian

b She likes to play chess

c She is a cellist

9. Where does Nick Fury first gather the Avengers?

a At a shawarma restaraunt

b On the S.H.I.E.L.D. helicarrier

c At Stark Tower

■■▢ 10. Who collects vintage Captain America cards?
a Agent Maria Hill
b Agent Phil Coulson
c Dr. Bruce Banner

■■▢ 11. What does Steve Rogers believe is 'powered by some sort of electricity'?
a Helicarrier tech
b Iron Man's armour
c The Chitauri Leviathan

■■▢ 12. How does Tony describe himself to Steve Rogers without his Iron Man armour?
a 'A hero.'
b 'Just a normal guy.'
c 'Genius, billionaire, playboy, philanthropist.'

■■▢ 13. Who doesn't understand Coulson's allusion to Stephen Hawking?
a Steve Rogers, aka Captain America
b Bruce Banner, aka Hulk
c Thor

■■■ 14. 'You're missing the point. There is no throne. There is no version of this where you come out on top.' Who says this to whom?
a Loki to Thor
b Tony Stark to Loki
c Captain America to Iron Man

15. How does Black Widow manage to climb onto a Chitauri jet?

a By riding the blast from Hawkeye's exploding arrow

b By hitching a ride on Thor's back

c By using Captain America's shield as a springboard

16. 'We are not a team, we are a time bomb.' Who says this?

a Bruce Banner, aka Hulk

b Clint Barton, aka Hawkeye

c Tony Stark, aka Iron Man

17. 'You brought the monster.' To whom is Loki referring?

a Thor

b Hulk

c Tony Stark

18. Who tries to calm Bruce Banner down to stop him from transforming into Hulk?

a Nick Fury

b Natasha Romanoff, aka Black Widow

c Steve Rogers, aka Captain America

19. What name is given to the climactic battle between the Avengers and the Chitauri?

a The Battle of New York

b The Battle of Manhattan

c The Battle of Brooklyn

20. What does Hulk call Loki after smashing him all over the floor?

a 'Tiny Idiot.'

b 'Weak Human.'

c 'Puny God.'

21. 'His first name is Agent.' Who is Tony talking about?

a Captain America

b Phil Coulson

c Nick Fury

22. During a short break when facing the Chitauri, who does Hulk punch sideways out of the frame?

a Thor

b Iron Man

c Loki

23. Where does the portal open?

a At the top of Stark Tower

b Over Central Park

c In the New York subway

24. 'I have an army.' How does Tony Stark reply to Loki?
  a   'So do we.'
  b   'We don't need one.'
  c   'We have a Hulk.'

25. Who does Nick Fury entrust the Tesseract to at the end of *Marvel's The Avengers*?
  a   Tony Stark, aka Iron Man
  b   Thor
  c   Steve Rogers, aka Captain America

26. 'I'm bringing the party to you!' What is Tony Stark talking about?
  a   His new Iron Man suit
  b   The Chitauri Leviathan
  c   An angry Hulk

27. 'That's the secret, Captain. I'm always angry.' Who says these words?
  a   Bruce Banner, aka Hulk
  b   Tony Stark, aka Iron Man
  c   Nick Fury

28. Who dies while trying to escape from Loki?

a   Clint Barton, aka Hawkeye
b   Agent Phil Coulson
c   Agent Maria Hill

29. 'Looks like Christmas, but with more… me.' Who says this?

a   Tony Stark, aka Iron Man
b   Natasha Romanoff, aka Black Widow
c   Steve Rogers, aka Captain America

30. Who closes the portal with Loki's sceptre?

a   Thor
b   Iron Man
c   Black Widow

31. On Stark Tower, which letter from the word STARK is not destroyed at the end of *Marvel's The Avengers*?

a   The A
b   The S
c   The K

32. 'Doth Mother know you wear-eth her drapes?' Who is Tony talking to?

a   Loki
b   Captain America
c   Thor

33. Which fearsome Marvel villain appears in the post-credits scene?

a Ronan the Accuser

b Thanos

c Galactus

34. Who grabs Iron Man during the Battle of New York and saves him from a fatal fall?

a Hulk

b Thor

c Captain America

35. In the post-credits scene, how does Thanos react to these words of the Other: 'To challenge humans is to court death.'

a He smiles

b He crushes the goblet he's holding

c He doesn't react

IRON MAN 3

1. What is the name of the project Maya Hansen is working on in 1999?
   a   Project Goliath
   b   Project Titanus
   c   Project Extremis

2. What new name is given to James 'Rhodey' Rhodes' alias, War Machine?
   a   Iron Patriot
   b   Iron Machine
   c   Iron Hero

3. What is the Iron Legion?
   a   A group opposing Tony Stark and his allies
   b   A group made up of all the armour designed by Tony Stark
   c   A group of avid Tony Stark fans

4. 'You know who I am, you don't know where I am and you'll never see me coming.' Who says this?
   a   Tony Stark
   b   The Mandarin
   c   Aldrich Killian

5. What is the acronym for the company created by Aldrich Killian?

a   AIM (Advanced Idea Mechanics)

b   GUM (General Unified Machines)

c   EAR (Electronics and Robotics)

6. Where does Tony crash-land after escaping the attack on his home?

a   Tennessee

b   Upstate New York

c   The Atlantic Ocean

7. What happens to Tony Stark's villa in Malibu in *Iron Man 3*?

a   It collapses in an earthquake

b   It is trashed during a wild house party

c   It is destroyed by the Mandarin

8. Which of Tony Stark's allies is injured in an attack by the Mandarin, resulting in a coma?

a   James 'Rhodey' Rhodes

b   Happy Hogan

c   Pepper Potts

9. What gift does Tony give to Pepper at Christmas?

a   An engagement ring

b   A gigantic plush rabbit

c   A custom Iron Man suit

■■◻ **10.** 'Einstein only slept three hours a year and he succeeded.' Who says this?
a Tony Stark
b The Mandarin
c Aldrich Killian

■■◻ **11.** Where did Tony celebrate New Year's Eve 1999?
a Bern, Switzerland
b Miami, USA
c London, England

■■■ **12.** 'Don't you remember? It hardly surprises me.'
'Don't be offended, I don't even know what I ate this morning any more.'
Who is Tony talking to?
a Aldrich Killian
b The Mandarin
c Maya Hansen

■■■ **13.** How many aeroplane passengers does Iron Man save?
a 13
b 23
c 33

14. What is the name of the young boy who becomes Tony's ally?

a Harrow

b Harley

c Himbo

15. How does Tony get rid of Aldrich Killian?

a He pushes him off the top of Stark Tower

b He traps him with an Iron Man armour which then explodes

c He has him arrested by the FBI for tax fraud

16. Who fell asleep while Tony Stark was telling him about the events of *Iron Man 3*?

a Nick Fury

b Thor

c Bruce Banner

17. How does Maya Hansen die?

a She is killed by a bullet fired by Aldrich Killian

b She drowns in the Hudson River

c She is caught in an explosion

18. What does Tony Stark blow up for a Christmas firework display?

a Stark Tower

b All his suits of armour

c The Tesseract

19. What gift does Tony give Harley at the end of *Iron Man 3*?

a A Mark II potato gun

b The glove from an Iron Man suit

c A slingshot

20. 'They can take my house, all my stuff and my toys... but there is one thing that will never be taken away from me.' Complete Tony's line:

a 'My friends.'

b 'My brain.'

c 'I am Iron Man.'

21. What is the name of the US soldier who died after his body was injected with Extremis and used as a weapon?

a Chad Davis

b Eric Savin

c Trevor Slattery

22. What does Tony tell Ellen Brandt could be the title of his autobiography?

a *I Am Iron Man*

b *A Cheap Trick and a Cheesy One-Liner*

c *Fall from Grace*

23. What is James 'Rhodey' Rhodes' password?
a   ironmanfan
b   WAR MACHINE ROX
c   IRON PATRIOT USA

24. Where does Tony track Trevor Slattery to?
a   Miami, Florida
b   LA, California
c   New York City

25. Where does Aldrich Killian intend to attack the President of the USA?
a   At the White House
b   On a visit to New York
c   Aboard *Air Force One*

THOR: THE DARK WORLD

1. 'She has no more reason to be in Asgard than a goat has to attend a banquet.'
Who says this about whom?
- **a** Odin about Jane Foster
- **b** Loki about Frigga
- **c** Thor about Darcy Lewis

2. What kind of creature is Malekith?
- **a** A Frost Giant
- **b** An Asgardian
- **c** A Dark Elf

3. Where is the epicentre of the Convergence?
- **a** Queens, New York
- **b** Greenwich, London
- **c** Silver Lake, Los Angeles

4. 'It is only because I worry that you have survived.'
Who is talking to whom?
- **a** Odin to his son Loki
- **b** Queen Frigga to her husband, Odin
- **c** Jane Foster to Loki

5. Which Infinity Stone does the Collector receive at the end of *Thor: The Dark World*?
a   The Reality Stone (Aether)
b   The Time Stone
c   The Space Stone

6. The appearance of portals between realms is a sign of which event that happens approximately every 5,000 years?
a   The opening of the Quantum Realm
b   Ragnarok – the destruction of Asgard
c   The Convergence – the alignment of the Realms

7. 'Or, perhaps that is not the beauty you seek.' Who says this and who are they referring to?
a   Heimdall about Jane Foster
b   Loki about his adoptive mother, Frigga
c   Thor about Jane Foster

8. 'You lied to me. I'm impressed.' Who is talking to who?
a   Thor to Odin
b   Malekith to Loki
c   Loki to Thor

9. Who does Thor fail to save from Algrim and Malekith?

   a   His father, Odin

   b   His mother, Queen Frigga

   c   Jane Foster

10. 'You betray me, and I will kill you.'
'When do we start?'
Who is this conversation between?

   a   Loki and Thor

   b   Malekith and Loki

   c   Jane Foster and Thor

11. Who bothers Jane Foster in the middle of a date?

   a   Thor

   b   Heimdall

   c   Darcy Lewis

12. Why does Malekith want to seize the Aether?

   a   To tear a hole in reality

   b   To plunge the universe into eternal night

   c   To court Death

13. Darcy has the terrible idea to throw which item into the Aether portal?
a The Tesseract
b Mjolnir
c Car keys

14. 'From here, I can see nine realms and ten trillion souls.' Who says this?
a Heimdall
b Odin
c Malekith

15. How does Dr. Jane Foster welcome Thor on his return from Asgard?
a She kisses him
b She slaps him
c She doesn't recognise him

16. Who runs stark naked between the stones of Stonehenge?
a Dr. Erik Selvig
b Loki
c Darcy Lewis

▰▰▱ **17.** 'It's all right. I'll tell Father what you did here today.'
How does Loki respond to Thor?

a 'He'll never believe you.'
b 'Maybe he'll finally be proud of me.'
c 'I didn't do it for him.'

▰▰▰ **18.** How does Loki respond when Sif warns him: 'Betray him, and I'll kill you.'

a 'It's good to see you, too, Sif.'
b 'Not if I kill you first.'
c 'No you won't.'

▰▰▱ **19.** When Loki amuses himself by changing shape, which Avenger does he turn himself into?

a Black Widow
b Captain America
c Hawkeye

▰▰▰ **20.** 'There are nine kingdoms. Our future King cannot only care about humans.'
Who says this to Thor?

a Sif
b Loki
c Heimdall

21. What does Loki tell Odin he wanted to be in Midgard?
 a   An all-powerful king
 b   A benevolent god
 c   A feared ruler

22. Who is Ian Boothby when we meet him?
 a   A waiter on Jane's date
 b   A reporter
 c   Darcy's intern

23. What is the name of Odin's father, Thor's grandfather?
 a   Bor
 b   Heimdall
 c   Odin the First

24. Who greets Thor with 'How's space?'
 a   Jane Foster
 b   Loki
 c   Darcy Lewis

25. Who gives the Aether to the Collector?
 a   Thor and Loki
 b   Sif and Volstagg
 c   The Warriors Three

CAPTAIN AMERICA: THE WINTER SOLDIER

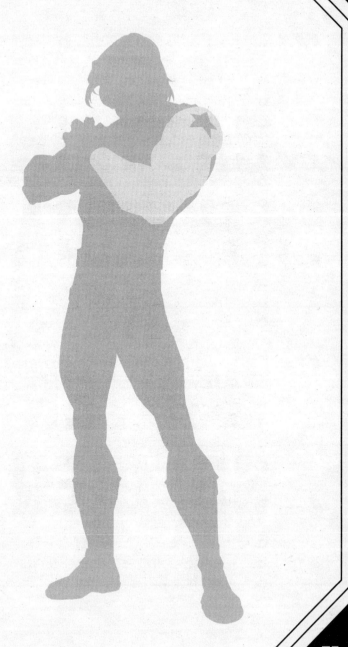

CAPTAIN AMERICA:
THE WINTER SOLDIER

▰▰▰ **1.** Who does Natasha Romanoff suggest Steve Rogers should ask out on a date?
- **a** Darcy Lewis
- **b** Kristen from Statistics
- **c** Natalie Rushman

▰▱▱ **2.** Who is Steve's next-door neighbour?
- **a** Sharon Carter, agent of S.H.I.E.L.D.
- **b** Nick Fury, director of S.H.I.E.L.D.
- **c** Sam Wilson, aka Falcon

▰▰▱ **3.** What is not damaged in Nick Fury's car?
- **a** The airbags
- **b** The air conditioning
- **c** The back wheels

▰▰▰ **4.** 'The world is so chaotic that humanity is now ready to give up its freedom to obtain security.' Who says this?
- **a** Senator Stern
- **b** Alexander Pierce
- **c** Arnim Zola

▰▱▱ **5.** Which relative of Sharon Carter knew Steve Rogers well?
- **a** Her aunt, Peggy Carter
- **b** Her grandfather, Bucky Barnes
- **c** Her mother, Peggy Carter

6. Who does Steve find in his apartment?
a The Winter Soldier
b Nick Fury
c Natasha Romanoff, aka Black Widow

7. When does Steve meet Sam Wilson?
a When he is out jogging
b When he is visiting Bucky's memorial
c When he is fighting the Winter Soldier

8. 'I'm looking for the Prehistoric Museum. I need to get a fossil.'
Who is Natasha Romanoff talking about?
a Bucky Barnes
b Alexander Pierce
c Steve Rogers

9. When does the S.T.R.I.K.E. team attack Captain America in the S.H.I.E.L.D. elevator?
a After his jog with Sam Wilson
b After his first fight with the Winter Soldier
c After his interview with Alexander Pierce

10. During the exhibition devoted to Captain America, who signals to a young visitor to remain silent?
a The real Steve Rogers
b Bucky Barnes
c A security guard

11. In the bunker that Steve and Natasha go into, which scientist has a data bank containing his consciousness?

a   Leo Fitz

b   Arnim Zola

c   Werner Reinhardt

12. Which organisation infiltrated S.H.I.E.L.D. in order to rule the world?

a   Hydra

b   Manticore

c   Griffon

13. 'Steve, you saved the world. What we have done with it is appalling.'
Who says this to Steve?

a   Sam Wilson

b   Nick Fury

c   Peggy Carter

14. Who does Steve visit in hospital?

a   Peggy Carter

b   Nick Fury

c   Bucky Barnes

15. On whose orders is Sharon Carter charged with protecting Steve?

a   Alexander Pierce

b   Nick Fury

c   Natasha Romanoff, aka Black Widow

16. 'Don't look at me like that. I do everything like him. Slower.' Who says this?

a Natasha Romanoff, aka Black Widow

b Nick Fury

c Sam Wilson, aka Falcon

17. Why does Natasha Romanoff ask Steve Rogers to kiss her?

a Because she's in love with him

b So they can go unnoticed through the crowd

c To try and bait the Winter Soldier

18. 'That is not freedom. It's terror.' Who does Steve Rogers say this to?

a Arnim Zola

b Nick Fury

c Alexander Pierce

19. Who is the Winter Soldier?

a Bucky Barnes

b Sam Wilson

c Sharon Carter

20. 'Is this little display meant to insinuate that you're gonna throw me off the roof? Because it's really not your style, Rogers.' 'You're right. It's not. It's hers.' Whose 'style' is Captain America referring to?

a Black Widow's

b Sharon Carter's

c Peggy Carter's

21. At the end of the film, what do Sam Wilson and Steve Rogers decide?

a To start their own version of S.H.I.E.L.D.

b To go looking for Bucky

c To retire from being heroes

22. 'Before we get started, does anyone want to get out?' Where does Captain America say these words?

a On the S.H.I.E.L.D. helicarrier

b In Natasha's car

c In the elevator at S.H.I.E.L.D.

23. Where does Steve hide the USB stick containing the S.H.I.E.L.D. secrets?

a In a pizza box

b In Sharon Carter's apartment

c In a vending machine

24. 'It's a funny way to live.'
'It's a funny way to not die.'
Who answers Steve Rogers like this?

a Natasha Romanoff

b Bucky Barnes

c Nick Fury

25. How does Steve cushion his fall from the S.H.I.E.L.D. elevator?

a With the body of one of his attackers

b With his shield

c With the elevator door

26. When corrupt S.H.I.E.L.D. agents encounter one another, what do they whisper?

a 'S.H.I.E.L.D. must fall.'

b 'Death to Captain America.'

c 'Hail Hydra.'

27. 'He said that peace was not an achievement but simply a mission.' Who says this about Steve Rogers?

a Nick Fury

b Peggy Carter

c Sam Wilson

28. Where does Bucky go in the last post-credits scene of the film?

a To his own grave

b To an exhibit dedicated to Captain America

c To Steve's home

29. 'You want to stop me, so stop me. You know where to find me.' Who says this?

a Bucky Barnes

b Steve Rogers

c Natasha Romanoff

30. Which Avengers make their first appearance in the post-credits scene?

a Wanda and Pietro Maximoff

b T'Challa (Black Panther) and Shuri

c Peter Quill (Star-Lord) and Gamora

GUARDIANS OF THE GALAXY

1. What gift did young Peter Quill's mother give him before her death?

a   A mix tape

b   A photograph of them together

c   A teddy bear

2. Which planet is Star-Lord on at the beginning of the film?

a   Earth

b   Titan

c   Morag

3. Which sinister individual is Gamora the adopted daughter of?

a   Ronan the Accuser

b   Nebula

c   Thanos

4. 'Stop smiling, you're supposed to be professional.' Who is talking to whom?

a   Rocket to Groot

b   Gamora to Star-Lord

c   Star-Lord to Drax

5. Which planet is the capital of the Nova Empire?

a   Morag

b   Xandar

c   Sakaar

6. What species is Ronan the Accuser?

a Asgardian

b Chitauri

c Kree

7. 'All that hatred, all that anger, it was just to forget my pain.' Who says this?

a Drax

b Ronan the Accuser

c Gamora

8. What does Star-Lord say the Ravagers' code is?

a 'Stick together.'

b 'Steal from everybody.'

c 'Trust nobody.'

9. When he crosses paths with a girl on the mining colony of the asteroid Knowhere, what does Groot offer her?

a A pickaxe

b A hug

c A flower he grows in his hand

10. What is the name of the Guardians of the Galaxy's ship?

a The *Star*

b The *Hawk*

c The *Milano*

11. 'Well, now I'm standing. Happy? We're all standing now. Bunch of jackasses, standing in a circle.' Who says this?
- **a** Star-Lord
- **b** Rocket
- **c** Drax

12. Who is Carina?
- **a** Thanos' pilot
- **b** Gamora's mother
- **c** The Collector's servant

13. What is the phrase that Groot uses to express himself?
- **a** 'I am Groot.'
- **b** 'I am a tree.'
- **c** 'We are friends.'

14. By which name do we better know Taneleer Tivan?
- **a** The Librarian
- **b** The Collector
- **c** The Archivist

15. 'Nothing goes over my head.' What does Rocket say to inspire this response from Drax?
- **a** 'That joke is gonna go over his head.'
- **b** 'Everything goes over his head.'
- **c** 'The metaphors are gonna go over his head.'

16. When Star-Lord talks about teaching an 'entire city full of people with sticks up their butts' to dance, how does Gamora react?

a 'Who put the sticks up their butts?'

b 'How did that help?'

c 'That sounds ridiculous.'

17. Who issues a bounty on Star-Lord's head?

a Yondu

b The Collector

c Ronan the Accuser

18. In the Collector's lair, who triggers a gigantic explosion when trying to steal the Orb?

a Star-Lord

b Gamora

c Carina

19. What is Drax's nickname?

a Drax the Destroyer

b Drax the Delinquent

c Drax the Dangerous

20. What unique collection of cosmic stones is the Orb a part of?

a The Eternity Gems

b The Infinity Stones

c The Limitless Rocks

21. 'Why would I put my finger on his throat?' Who says this?

a Rocket

b Gamora

c Drax

22. What prison do the Guardians of the Galaxy escape from?

a The Kyln

b Prison 42

c The Raft

23. 'Quill. I have lived most of my life surrounded by my enemies. I will be grateful to die among my friends.' Who says this?

a Gamora

b Drax

c Rocket

24. To escape, what object does Rocket ask for that he doesn't need?

a A guard's security band

b The prosthetic leg of a prisoner

c The battery from a security camera

25. During the fall of the *Dark Aster*, what does Groot say to Rocket when he asks why he is sacrificing himself?

a   'I am Groot.'
b   'We are Groot.'
c   'You are Groot.'

26. At the end of *Guardians of the Galaxy*, who does Peter Quill trust with the Orb?

a   Gamora
b   The Nova Corps
c   The Avengers

27. How does Star-Lord distract Ronan the Accuser?

a   By challenging him to a duel to the death
b   By challenging him to a chess game
c   By challenging him to a dance battle

28. Which of Drax's relatives did Ronan the Accuser kill?

a   His father and brother
b   His wife and daughter
c   His three sons

29. Who comments that they will die in the company of the biggest idiots in the galaxy?

a   Gamora

b   Drax

c   Rocket

30. 'What do you mean, it's still better than 11%? What kind of thinking is that?' Who is Rocket talking to?

a   Groot

b   Star-Lord

c   Drax

31. At the end of *Guardians of the Galaxy*, who stops dancing as soon as Drax looks at him?

a   Rocket

b   Star-Lord

c   Baby Groot

32. In the post-credits scene, who doesn't understand why the Collector lets Cosmo the dog lick his face?

a   Thanos

b   Howard the Duck

c   Grandmaster

33. Who sent Nebula and Gamora to work for Ronan the Accuser?

a Thanos

b Yondu

c Korath

34. Approximately, how long have the Kree and Nova empires been at war?

a 1,000 years

b 2,000 years

c 3,000 years

35. What is Star-Lord Peter Quill's mother's first name?

a Amanda

b Andromeda

c Meredith

AVENGERS: AGE OF ULTRON

1. What are the Avengers looking for in Sokovia at the start of *Avengers: Age of Ultron*?

a Loki's sceptre

b Thor's hammer, Mjolnir

c The twins, Wanda and Pietro Maximoff

2. Who bans swearing?

a Nick Fury

b Captain America

c Hawkeye

3. Who, or what, is Ultron's first victim?

a JARVIS

b Stark Tower

c Pepper Potts

4. Which Avenger helps Tony Stark create Ultron?

a Steve Rogers, aka Captain America

b Natasha Romanoff, aka Black Widow

c Bruce Banner, aka Hulk

5. When the Avengers are trying to stop Tony Stark from activating Vision, who brings Vision to life?

a Thor

b Bruce Banner

c Pepper Potts

6. Who kills Baron Strucker?

a Wanda Maximoff

b Ultron

c Ulysses Klaue

7. From which small European country does Ultron intend to carry out his plans?

a   Latveria

b   Luxembourg

c   Sokovia

8. 'If they hurt you, you hurt them. If they kill you...' Complete this line from Captain America.

a   '... you get up!'

b   '... you kill them!'

c   '... you die!'

9. What is the name of the satellite, designed by Tony Stark and Bruce Banner, to deploy a powerful suit of armour in case Hulk loses control completely?

a   Monica

b   Veronica

c   Shirley

10. How does Ultron plan to bring peace to the world?

a   By killing Tony Stark

b   By destroying the Avengers

c   By eliminating humanity

11. What does Vision wear on his forehead?

a   The Mind Stone, one of the six Infinity Stones

b   A bullseye

c   A little hat

12. Which future Avengers join forces with Ultron before turning against him?

a   T'Challa, aka Black Panther, and Shuri

b   Star-Lord and Gamora

c   Wanda and Pietro Maximoff

13. Who sells vibranium to Ultron?

a   Tony Stark

b   Ulysses Klaue

c   Pietro Maximoff

14. What is the name of Clint Barton's wife?

a   Katie

b   Jessica

c   Laura

15. What safe haven does Clint Barton, aka Hawkeye, take the Avengers to?

a   His family's farmhouse

b   An underground bunker

c   His mother's apartment

16. Before the events of Avengers: Age of Ultron, who was the only Avenger who knew about the existence of Clint Barton's family?

a   Natasha Romanoff, aka Black Widow

b   Tony Stark, aka Iron Man

c   Steve Rogers, aka Captain America

▰▰▱ **17.** When the Avengers take turns trying to lift Mjolnir, who makes Thor worry for a moment?

   a   Bruce Banner, aka Hulk

   b   Steve Rogers, aka Captain America

   c   Natasha Romanoff, aka Black Widow

▰▱▱ **18.** Who is waiting for Tony Stark in the barn at Clint Barton's farm?

   a   Ultron

   b   Nick Fury

   c   Vision

▰▰▱ **19.** Which famous Nietzsche quote does Ultron use?

   a   'What doesn't kill me makes me stronger.'

   b   'Hope in reality is the worst of all evils.'

   c   'To live is to suffer, to survive is to find meaning in the suffering.'

▰▱▱ **20.** How does Vision overcome the reluctance of the Avengers to join their ranks?

   a   When he saves Clint Barton's life

   b   When he stands up to Ultron

   c   When he lifts Thor's hammer

▰▱▱ **21.** In Sokovia, who sacrifices themselves to save Clint Barton and the child he is protecting?

   a   Wanda Maximoff

   b   Pietro Maximoff

   c   Natasha Romanoff, aka Black Widow

22. 'If you walk through that door, you become an Avenger.' Who is Clint Barton talking to?

a   Wanda Maximoff

b   Pietro Maximoff

c   Ultron

23. In which Asian capital do the Avengers face Ultron?

a   Tokyo, Japan

b   Seoul, South Korea

c   Beijing, China

24. Which trauma does Natasha Romanoff relive during a hallucination?

a   The Red Room

b   Watching her family die

c   The Battle of New York

25. 'I pulled her out of mothballs with a couple of old friends. She's dusty, but she'll do.' What is Nick Fury talking about?

a   The Mark I Iron Man armour

b   Captain America's shield

c   The S.H.I.E.L.D. helicarrier

26. What is 'terribly well-balanced', according to Vision?

a   Thor's hammer

b   The S.H.I.E.L.D. helicarrier

c   A sword given to him by Tony Stark

▰▰▱ **27.** Who takes charge of the new Avengers HQ at the end of *Avengers: Age of Ultron*?

a   Iron Man and Captain America

b   Iron Man and Black Widow

c   Captain America and Black Widow

▰▰▰ **28.** What does Wanda do to Ultron?

a   She disintegrates him

b   She rips out his 'heart'

c   She cuts off his head

▰▰▱ **29.** At the end of the film, who are the four new Avengers who are about to be trained in the group's new HQ?

a   Vision, Wanda Maximoff, Sam Wilson (Falcon) and James 'Rhodey' Rhodes (War Machine)

b   Peter Parker (Spider-Man), Wanda Maximoff, Pietro Maximoff and Vision

c   Wanda Maximoff, Peter Parker (Spider-Man), Sam Wilson (Falcon) and Vision

▰▱▱ **30.** Whose hand do we see in the post-credits scene of the film?

a   Tony Stark's hand, in a new Iron Man armour

b   Thanos' hand, wearing the Infinity Gauntlet

c   Ant-Man's hand, grasping something very tiny

ANT-MAN

1. How many years had Scott Lang served behind bars before his release?

a   One

b   Three

c   Five

2. Where is Scott when he tries on the suit he just stole?

a   In the bathtub

b   In a broom cupboard

c   In a toilet cubicle

3. Why is Scott Lang in prison at the start of *Ant-Man*?

a   Theft

b   Murder

c   Identity fraud

4. Where is Hank Pym 'supposed to be' when he tenders his resignation to Howard Stark?

a   London

b   New York

c   Moscow

5. Name a member of S.H.I.E.L.D. that Hank Pym faces in the opening scene.
(Three possible answers)

6. Who picks Scott up from prison?
- **a** Maggie
- **b** Luis
- **c** Jim Paxton

7. What is Cassie's mother's new partner, Paxton's, job?
- **a** Police officer
- **b** Firefighter
- **c** School teacher

8. What happens when Scott tries on the stolen suit?
- **a** He gains super strength
- **b** He turns into an ant
- **c** His body shrinks to the size of an ant

9. What present does Scott give Cassie for her birthday?
- **a** A dollhouse
- **b** A cuddly rabbit
- **c** A train set

10. What name does Darren Cross give to the suit he created?
- **a** Yellowjacket
- **b** The Wasp
- **c** Lady Bug

11. 'Are you trying to find my daddy?'
'Uh, yeah I am, sweetheart. I just want your daddy to be safe.'
How does Cassie reply to Paxton?
a 'I want him to be safe too.'
b 'Leave him alone.'
c 'Hope you don't catch him.'

12. What does Scott Lang rename the flying ant #247?
a Gr-Ant
b Ant-Thony
c Ant-Drew

13. In Cassie's room, what toy are Ant-Man and Yellowjacket fighting over?
a A teddy bear
b A miniature train
c A toy car

14. 'It's not too often that you rob a place, and then get welcomed back.'
Who says this?
a Luis
b Scott
c Darren Cross

15. What do the ants draw for Scott on the floor of his cell?
- **a** A map of the jail
- **b** A countdown to his escape
- **c** A little picture of a cat

16. When Scott wakes up at Hank's, what are the sentry ants doing at the foot of his bed?
- **a** They are guarding him in Hope's absence
- **b** They are playing cards
- **c** They are bringing him food

17. When did Hope van Dyne take up martial arts?
- **a** While travelling in Asia
- **b** At university, while studying engineering
- **c** After the death of her mother, Janet

18. Which colour discs made by Hank make their target expand?
- **a** The red discs
- **b** The blue discs
- **c** The yellow discs

19. Which Super Hero intercepts Scott at the new Avengers Compound?
- **a** Clint Barton, aka Hawkeye
- **b** Natasha Romanoff, aka Black Widow
- **c** Sam Wilson, aka Falcon

20. How did Janet van Dyne, the first Wasp, disappear?
- **a** By getting squashed by a fly swatter while in Wasp form
- **b** By flying into a jet engine
- **c** By shrinking her body to subatomic size so she could defuse a bomb

21. 'You have a poetic soul. You should write poetry.' Who is talking to whom?
- **a** Scott Lang to Hope van Dyne
- **b** Luis to Scott Lang
- **c** Hope van Dyne to Hank Pym

22. How does Scott get rid of Yellowjacket?
- **a** By squashing him
- **b** By running him over with a toy train
- **c** By shrinking his body to subatomic size

23. At the end of Ant-Man, which Super Hero is Hope van Dyne going to take over from?
- **a** Ant-Man
- **b** The Wasp
- **c** Falcon

▮▮▮▯ **24.** What ants does Ant-Man use to fry Pym Technologies' computers?

   a   'Crazy ants' (*Paratrechina longicornis*)

   b   Fire ants (*Solenopsis mandibularis*)

   c   Carpenter ants (*Camponotus pennsylvanicus*)

▮▮▮ **25.** What type of ants allow Ant-Man to create bridges or rafts?

   a   'Crazy ants' (*Paratrechina longicornis*)

   b   Fire ants (*Solenopsis mandibularis*)

   c   Carpenter ants (*Camponotus pennsylvanicus*)

CAPTAIN AMERICA: CIVIL WAR

1. Who falls in love with Wanda Maximoff?
- **a** Vision
- **b** Hawkeye
- **c** Captain America

2. Which Super Hero makes his first appearance in the film?
- **a** Falcon
- **b** Ant-Man
- **c** Black Panther

3. 'Death in our culture is not the end. For us, it's more of a starting point.'
Who is talking to whom?
- **a** T'Challa to Natasha Romanoff
- **b** Bucky Barnes to Steve Rogers
- **c** Vision to Wanda Maximoff

4. When he meets Tony Stark, how long has Peter Parker had Spider-Man's superpowers?
- **a** One month
- **b** Six months
- **c** One year

5. Who are the witnesses to Steve Rogers and Sharon Carter's first kiss?
- **a** Natasha Romanoff and Tony Stark
- **b** Sam Wilson and Bucky Barnes
- **c** Wanda Maximoff and Vision

6. Who leads the mercenary commando that the Avengers neutralise in Nigeria?

a   Bucky Barnes, aka the Winter Soldier

b   Brock Rumlow, aka Crossbones

c   Helmut Zemo

7. Who obtains the code that allows him to activate the Winter Soldier?

a   Helmut Zemo

b   Captain America

c   Brock Rumlow, aka Crossbones

8. 'Who are you? Spider-Boy?' Who is talking to Peter Parker, aka Spider-Man?

a   Steve Rogers

b   Sam Wilson

c   Tony Stark

9. 'Sometimes I want to punch you in your perfect teeth.' Who is talking to whom?

a   Sam Wilson to Bucky Barnes

b   Tony Stark to Steve Rogers

c   Natasha Romanoff to Clint Barton

10. Where does Tony get confronted by the mother of an accidental victim of the Battle of Sokovia?

a   Outside Stark Tower

b   At a conference at a university

c   At a party in Miami

11. 'I don't know if you've ever been in a fight, but we usually don't talk so much.'
Who says this to Spider-Man?
a   Sam Wilson, aka Falcon
b   Steve Rogers, aka Captain America
c   Bucky Barnes, aka the Winter Soldier

12. What new power does Ant-Man have in *Captain America: Civil War*?
a   He can fly
b   He can grow to a gigantic size
c   He can shoot ants from his hands

13. How many nations approved the Sokovia Agreement?
a   117
b   127
c   137

14. Whose funeral does Steve Rogers attend in London?
a   Bucky Barnes'
b   A boy who was killed in the Battle of Sokovia's
c   Peggy Carter's

15. During the airport battle, which Avengers object does Spider-Man manage to grab?
a   One of Falcon's wings
b   Captain America's shield
c   The Winter Soldier's vibranium arm

16. True or false? During the airport battle, Hawkeye is on Captain America's side.

17. Which Avenger is seriously injured during the airport battle?
a   Bucky Barnes, aka the Winter Soldier
b   Scott Lang, aka Ant-Man
c   James 'Rhodey' Rhodes, aka War Machine

18. 'Vengeance has consumed you. It's consuming them. I am done letting it consume me.' Who says this to whom?
a   Bucky Barnes to Steve Rogers
b   T'Challa to Helmut Zemo
c   James 'Rhodey' Rhodes to Tony Stark

19. Which world leader dies in the Vienna bombing?
a   The Queen of the United Kingdom
b   The President of the United States
c   King T'Chaka of Wakanda

20. 'That shield doesn't belong to you. You don't deserve it. My father made that shield.' How does Captain America react when Tony says this?
a   He leaves the shield behind
b   He snaps the shield in half
c   He cries

21. Who wins the final duel?
- **a** Captain America
- **b** Tony Stark
- **c** Nobody

22. Who is stirring trouble in the background for the Avengers?
- **a** Brock Rumlow, aka Crossbones
- **b** Bucky Barnes, aka the Winter Soldier
- **c** Helmut Zemo

23. In *Captain America: Civil War*, which Avengers are missing?
- **a** Vision and Wanda Maximoff
- **b** Thor and Hulk
- **c** Black Widow and Hawkeye

24. What does Tony Stark tell Peter Parker's aunt he's visiting Peter to discuss?
- **a** His identity as Spider-Man
- **b** His application to college
- **c** A grant for the September Foundation

25. 'Longing, rusted, furnace, daybreak, seventeen, benign, nine, homecoming, one, freight car.' What does this list of words relate to?
- **a** Titles of future Avengers movies
- **b** Hydra code words
- **c** Trigger words that activate the Winter Soldier's brainwashing

26. 'If you need us, if you need me, I'll be there.' Who writes these words and to whom?

a Thor to the other Avengers

b Steve to Tony

c Tony to Steve

27. Who says, 'If we can't accept limitations, we're boundaryless, we're no better than the bad guys'?

a Captain America

b Tony Stark

c T'Challa

28. Who says, 'Victory at the expense of the innocent is no victory at all'?

a King T'Chaka of Wakanda

b T'Challa

c Tony Stark

29. In which borough of New York do Peter and his aunt, May, live?

a Queens

b Brooklyn

c Staten Island

30. What does Vision need to spice up his dish?

a A bottle of hot sauce

b Red chillies

c Paprika

DOCTOR STRANGE

1. What is Stephen Strange's profession?
- **a** Neurosurgeon
- **b** Mechanical engineer
- **c** Biochemist

2. Who rules the Dark Dimension?
- **a** The Ancient One
- **b** Kaecilius
- **c** Dormammu

3. What does Doctor Strange use as his mantra?
- **a** The name of his friend and love interest: 'Christine'
- **b** The wifi code: 'shamballa'
- **c** His coffee order: 'flat white'

4. 'Arrogance and fear still keep you from learning the simplest and most significant lesson of all.'
'Which is?'
What does The Ancient One say in response?
- **a** 'You're not important.'
- **b** 'It's not just about you.'
- **c** 'You don't need magic.'

5. 'At the root of existence, mind and matter meet. Thoughts shape reality.' When does The Ancient One say this?

   a   After opening Stephen Strange's third eye

   b   When she first meets Stephen Strange

   c   Right before she dies

6. 'Might I offer you some advice? Forget everything you think you know.' Who says this to Stephen Strange?

   a   The Ancient One

   b   Wong

   c   Mordo

7. Who watches over the library of Kamar-Taj?

   a   Wong

   b   Mordo

   c   Kaecilius

8. In what dimension does Stephen Strange train in magic?

   a   The Dark Dimension

   b   The Mirror Dimension

   c   Asgard

9. Where is the shrine of The Ancient One?

   a   In New York City, USA

   b   In Kamar-Taj, Kathmandu

   c   In Guangzhou, China

10. Who is Stephen on the phone to when he crashes his car?
a Billy, a colleague from the hospital
b Dr. Christine Palmer
c A telemarketer

11. How does Stephen Strange stay alive when his body is dying and Dr. Christine Palmer is trying to save him?
a In his astral form
b Using breathing exercises
c By taking medication

12. 'We never lose our demons. We only learn to live above them.' Who says this?
a Wong
b Dr. Christine Palmer
c The Ancient One

13. Who tells Stephen Strange that his hand injuries are irreversible?
a Dr. Christine Palmer
b Jonathan Pangborn
c Mordo

14. What is the first Sanctum Sanctorum to be destroyed?
a The New York Sanctum
b The Hong Kong Sanctum
c The London Sanctum

15. 'But look at me. Stretching one moment out into a thousand... just so that I can watch the snow.' Who says this and what are they talking about?
a Kaecilius, talking about making contact with the Dark Dimension
b The Ancient One, talking about her own death
c Stephen Strange, talking about astral projection

16. How does Doctor Strange manage to save Earth from Dormammu?
a By using the Cloak of Levitation
b By convincing Kaecilius of his wrongdoing
c With a time loop

17. What does Wong reveal to Doctor Strange about the Eye of Agamotto?
a That it holds one of the six Infinity Stones
b That it was never real
c That it can be used to travel into space

18. Which Avenger visits Doctor Strange at home at the end of the film?

a   Tony Stark, aka Iron Man

b   Steve Rogers, aka Captain America

c   Thor

19. 'But you will suffer.'

'Pain is an old friend.'

Who is Doctor Strange talking to?

a   Kaecilius

b   Dormammu

c   The Ancient One

20. Where does The Ancient One leave Stephen Strange, in order to force him to use his magic to avoid freezing to death?

a   In the middle of the Arctic

b   On the Moon

c   At the top of Mount Everest

21. Who steals two pages of Cagliostro's book from the Kamar-Taj library?

a   Kaecilius

b   Wong

c   Stephen Strange

22. In which Sanctum Sanctorum does Doctor Strange receive his Cloak of Levitation?

a The New York Sanctum Sanctorum

b The Hong Kong Sanctum Sanctorum

c The London Sanctum Sanctorum

23. What is the address of the New York Sanctum Sanctorum?

a 27B Madison Avenue

b 276C Maiden Lane

c 177A Bleecker Street

24. 'Time will tell how much I love you.' Where did Dr. Christine Palmer have this phrase engraved?

a In the doorway of the New York Sanctum Sanctorum

b On the back of Stephen Strange's watch

c On the inside of her ring

25. 'This is where you ask me to forgive you.' 'This is where I ask you to go home.' Who is Stephen Strange talking to?

a Wong

b Dr. Christine Palmer

c Mordo

GUARDIANS OF THE GALAXY VOL. 2

GUARDIANS OF THE GALAXY
VOL. 2

■□□ **1.** What are Mantis' powers?
- **a** Telepathy: she can read others' thoughts
- **b** The power of empathy: she can understand and alter the emotions of others
- **c** Telekinesis: she can move objects with her mind

■□□ **2.** 'I'm what they call a Celestial, honey.' Who says this?
- **a** Ego
- **b** Yondu
- **c** Peter Quill, aka Star-Lord

■■□ **3. True or false?** Baby Groot has not retained the memories of adult Groot.

■■□ **4.** What is the name of the Ravager pirate who triggers Rocket's fit of laughter?
- **a** Kraglin
- **b** Stakar
- **c** Taserface

■■□ **5.** What does Mantis reveal about Peter that makes Drax laugh so much?
- **a** His fear of Rocket
- **b** His feelings for Gamora
- **c** That he still misses his mother

6. What does Baby Groot do while the other Guardians fight the monster Abilisk?

a Hides

b Cheers them on

c Dances

7. Who is the boss of all the Ravagers?

a Kraglin

b Stakar

c Taserface

8. What does Drax think of Mantis?

a Strange and intense

b Quiet and wholesome

c Ugly and innocent

9. What happens to the cassette player that Peter never lets out of his sight?

a A furious Ego smashes it

b It is destroyed by Yondu's arrow

c It gets lost in the mess of Peter's bedroom

10. Who saves the Guardians from an attack by the Sovereign?

a Yondu

b Nebula

c Ego

11. Where does Drax tell Star-Lord he met his beloved?
a   At a war rally
b   At a dance
c   At school

12. What does Rocket desperately ask all the Guardians for before Baby Groot goes to plant a bomb on Ego's core?
a   A battery
b   Tape
c   A snack

13. On which planet do the Guardians meet Ego?
a   Knowhere
b   Contraxia
c   Berhert

14. Who turned out to have actually killed Meredith Quill, Peter's mother, and how?
a   Peter, in an accidental kitchen explosion
b   Nebula, by drugging her coffee
c   Ego, by implanting a tumour in her brain

15. What does Baby Groot become at the end of the film?

a   A teenager

b   A full-grown Groot

c   A potted plant

16. Who does Peter give Yondu's arrow to?

a   Rocket

b   Kraglin, Yondu's second in command

c   Gamora

17. Who does Kraglin accidentally hit when learning to master Yondu's arrow?

a   Drax

b   Peter

c   Rocket

18. Who is the High Priestess of the Sovereign?

a   Mantis

b   Ayesha

c   Gamora

19. What happened to Ego's thousands of children, apart from Peter?

a   They became powerful Celestials

b   They destroyed each other

c   Ego killed them all

20. What does Nebula decide to do at the end of the film?

a   Kill Thanos

b   Track down the Infinity Stones

c   Retire

21. When Ego invites Peter to his planet, which Guardians remain on Berhert alongside Nebula, their prisoner?

a   Rocket and Baby Groot

b   Gamora and Rocket

c   Baby Groot and Gamora

22. What does the Sovereign ask the Guardians to protect in exchange for Nebula?

a   Eggs

b   Batteries

c   Money

23. What affectionate name did Ego use for Meredith, Peter's mother?

a   River Lily

b   Cupcake

c   Songbird

24. What does Rocket taunt Taserface about?

a   His shoes

b   His name

c   His relationship with Yondu

25. What does Ayesha name the being she created to destroy the Guardians in the post-credits sequence?

a   Adam

b   David

c   Christopher

THOR: RAGNAROK

1. Where does Hulk eventually land after we see him aboard the Quinjet disappearing over the horizon in *Captain America: Civil War*?

a Outside Kathmandu
b Asgard
c Sakaar

2. Which saying, coined by Natasha Romanoff, does Thor keep repeating to Bruce Banner to help calm him down?

a 'Easy, big guy.'
b 'The sun's getting really low.'
c 'You're going to be okay.'

3. 'I need just one strand of your hair.'
'Let me explain something. My hair is not to be meddled with.'
Who is Thor replying to?

a Loki
b Valkyrie
c Doctor Strange

4. Who is Thor's older sister, the eldest daughter of Odin?

a Hela, Goddess of Death
b Valkyrie
c Freyja, Goddess of Marriage

5. 'Darling, you have no idea what's possible.' What does Hela do when she says this?

a She makes Odin disappear

b She smashes Thor's hammer

c She attacks Loki

6. What role does Hela assign to Skurge – a role she once carried out for Odin?

a Executioner

b Bodyguard

c Head of Security

7. In which country on Earth do Thor and Loki find their dying father?

a The USA

b Iceland

c Norway

8. What ship do Thor and Loki encounter on their return to Earth in the post-credits scene?

a *Sanctuary II*, Thanos' ship

b The *Milano*, the Guardians of the Galaxy's ship

c The Avengers' Quinjet

9. What does Surtur need to fulfil the prophecy of Ragnarok?

a The death of Thor and Odin

b To unite his crown with the Eternal Flame

c To be freed from his chains

10. 'The hammer pulled you off?' Who asks this?

a Loki

b Korg

c The Grandmaster

11. Which giant wolf was once the mount of Hela, Goddess of Death?

a Fenris

b Varcolac

c Angerboda

12. Who created the Contest of Champions?

a Odin

b Hela

c The Grandmaster

13. 'I know him! He's a friend from work!' Who is Thor talking about?

a Captain America

b Hulk

c Iron Man

14. Which eye does Thor lose during his battle with Hela?

a   His right eye
b   His left eye
c   His third eye

15. By what name is Thor announced by the Grandmaster in the Sakaar arena?

a   Strongest Avenger
b   Prince of Asgard
c   Lord of Thunder

16. Who destroys Asgard at the end of *Thor: Ragnarok*?

a   Hela
b   Surtur
c   Thanos

17. What has become of Hulk when Thor finds him on Sakaar?

a   He has become a gladiator in the Sakaar arena
b   He is living alone in the woods
c   He has been in a coma for years

18. What does the prophecy of Ragnarok mean for the Asgardians?
- **a** The death of their true ruler
- **b** The death of all Asgardians
- **c** The end of Asgard

19. Who is Scrapper 142?
- **a** Bruce Banner, aka Hulk
- **b** The Grandmaster's right-hand woman
- **c** The last of the Valkyries

20. What destination do Thor and the Asgardian people choose at the end of the film?
- **a** Deep space
- **b** Earth
- **c** The Moon

21. What's the Devil's Anus?
- **a** The biggest cosmic portal of Sakaar
- **b** The Grandmaster's best ship
- **c** A Sakaarian delicacy

22. 'So, last time I saw you, you were trying to kill everyone. Where are you at these days?'
How does Loki respond to Bruce Banner?
a 'Biding my time.'
b 'It varies from moment to moment.'
c 'Still trying to kill everyone.'

23. Who organises the rescue of the Asgardian people who are under threat from Hela?
a Loki
b Heimdall
c The Warriors Three

24. 'Asgard is not a place, it's a people.' Who says this?
a Valkyrie
b Loki
c Thor

25. What kingdom does Surtur rule over?
a Niflheim, the world of ice
b Jotunheim, the world of the Frost Giants
c Muspelheim, the world of fire

BLACK PANTHER

1. What is Wakanda's main resource?
a   Oil
b   Vibranium
c   Gold

2. What do Captain America's shield and Black Panther's armour have in common?
a   They share an essential component: vibranium
b   They were both designed by Stark Industries
c   They were both destroyed prior to the film

3. Who are Shuri and Ramonda?
a   T'Challa's friend and aunt
b   T'Challa's ex-girlfriend and bodyguard
c   T'Challa's sister and mother

4. What did Ulysses Klaue replace his left arm with?
a   A metal claw
b   A sonic cannon
c   Several knives

5. What is Everett K. Ross' profession?
  a   Officer in the Marines
  b   Insurance investigator
  c   CIA agent

6. 'A man who has not prepared his children for his own death has failed as a father.' Who says this?
  a   King T'Chaka
  b   Queen Ramonda
  c   T'Challa

7. What is so special about the 'heart-shaped herb'?
  a   It makes anyone who consumes it immortal
  b   It enhances the physical capabilities of anyone who consumes it
  c   It is extremely poisonous

8. Who threw T'Challa from the top of the Warrior Falls?
  a   Erik Killmonger, aka N'Jadaka
  b   M'Baku
  c   W'Kabi

9. What special feature does Black Panther's suit possess?

a It is bullet proof

b It absorbs and stores the kinetic energy from any attacks

c It makes him invisible

10. Who are the Dora Milaje?

a The various heirs to the Wakandan throne

b The army of the Border Tribe

c An elite group of female Wakandan warriors who serve the throne

11. Where does T'Challa try to intercept Ulysses Klaue?

a In a karaoke bar in New York City

b In an underground casino in Busan, South Korea

c In a dim sum restaurant in Hangzhou, China

12. 'You're a good man with a good heart and it's hard for a good man to be king.' Who says this to T'Challa?

a Ramonda

b Zuri

c T'Chaka

◢◢◢ **13.** 'What happens now determines what happens to the rest of the world.' Who says this?

   a   Erik Killmonger

   b   T'Challa, aka Black Panther

   c   Nakia

◢◢◪ **14.** 'Guns? So primitive!' Who says this?

   a   Okoye

   b   Erik Killmonger

   c   Ulysses Klaue

◢◪◪ **15.** Which Wakandan tribe lives in exile in the mountains?

   a   The Jabari

   b   The Border Tribe

   c   The River Tribe

◢◢◪ **16.** Who is the head of the Jabari?

   a   T'Challa

   b   W'Kabi

   c   M'Baku

◢◢◪ **17.** What do the Wakandan children call Bucky Barnes at the end of *Black Panther*?

   a   Winter Soldier

   b   White Wolf

   c   Silent Warrior

18. How does T'Challa react when a member of the UN asks him what a small developing nation can offer the world?

a He gets angry
b He rolls his eyes
c He smiles

19. How many African tribes originally settled in Wakanda?

a Five
b Seven
c Nine

20. What is Erik Killmonger's real name?

a Everett K. Ross
b N'Jobu
c Erik Stevens, aka N'Jadaka

21. Who strongly opposed the isolationist policy of Wakanda?

a Queen Ramonda
b M'Baku, head of the Jabari
c Prince N'Jobu, brother of King T'Chaka

22. What sport does the young Erik Stevens play in the United States?

a Basketball
b Baseball
c Soccer

23. What is Erik 'Killmonger' Stevens' last wish?
a   To die a noble death
b   To make peace with his cousin, T'Challa
c   To watch the sunset in Wakanda

24. Who designs T'Challa's suit, weapons and equipment?
a   He does
b   His sister, Shuri
c   His ex-lover, Nakia

25. What crucial decision does T'Challa make at the end of *Black Panther*?
a   To end Wakanda's isolationist policy
b   To give up his role as Black Panther
c   To pass up his crown to his sister

26. Whose heart is T'Challa trying to win back?
a   Nakia
b   Okoye
c   Ayo

27. In *Black Panther*, how old is Shuri, the technological genius from Wakanda?
a   21
b   18
c   16

28. Who is the general of the Dora Milaje?
a   Ayo
b   Okoye
c   Nakia

29. What is Okoye's weapon of choice?
a   Spear
b   Sword
c   Daggers

30. What are Shuri's weapons?
a   A sonic cannon and vibranium shield
b   A sonic spear and vibranium gloves
c   A vibranium shield and vibranium spear

31. 'And all this death just so I could kill you!'
Who says this?
a   T'Challa
b   Erik Killmonger
c   M'Baku

32. How was vibranium brought to Wakanda?
a   A meteorite landed there
b   Prehistoric people carried it there
c   It grew from the Earth's core

33. Where is the museum where Erik Killmonger and Ulysses Klaue steal a Wakandan artefact?

a New York City
b Paris
c London

34. What colour is the liquid from the 'heart-shaped herb' given to Black Panther?

a Purple
b Black
c Green

35. What kind of animal does W'Kabi train?

a Elephants
b Rhinoceroses
c Lions

AVENGERS: INFINITY WAR

1. How many Infinity Stones are there?
  a   Five
  b   Six
  c   Seven

2. What does Thanos want to do with the power of the Infinity Stones?
  a   He wants to destroy all of humanity
  b   He wants to become the ruler of the entire universe
  c   He wants to 'restore balance' by decimating half the universe

3. What colour is the Soul Stone?
  a   Red
  b   Orange
  c   Blue

4. What colour is the Power Stone?
  a   Purple
  b   Green
  c   Orange

5. What colour is the Mind Stone?
  a   Yellow
  b   Blue
  c   Green

6. What colour is the Time Stone?
a   Purple
b   Red
c   Green

7. What colour is the Reality Stone?
a   Blue
b   Red
c   Yellow

8. What colour is the Tesseract?
a   Blue
b   Orange
c   Purple

9. At the beginning of *Avengers: Infinity War*, who has the Reality Stone?
a   Red Skull
b   Tony Stark
c   The Collector

10. At the beginning of *Avengers: Infinity War*, who is guarding the Power Stone?
a   Thor and Loki
b   The Nova Corps
c   Vision

11. At the beginning of *Avengers: Infinity War*, where is the Mind Stone?

a In Loki's staff

b In the Eye of Agamotto

c On Vision's forehead

12. At the beginning of *Avengers: Infinity War*, who is protecting the Time Stone?

a Doctor Strange, in the Eye of Agamotto

b The Nova Corps

c Vision

13. At the beginning of *Avengers: Infinity War*, who has the Space Stone?

a Loki

b Iron Man

c The Nova Corps

14. Which nickname does Thor give to Rocket?

a Possum

b Hamster

c Rabbit

15. Who knows how to speak Groot's language?

a Thor

b Star-Lord

c Doctor Strange

▰▱▱ **16.** What must Thanos do to get the Soul Stone?

   a   He must tell Stonekeeper an unspoken truth

   b   He must sacrifice someone he loves

   c   He must defeat his greatest enemy

▰▰▱ **17.** What does Hulk say when Bruce Banner wants to transform?

   a   'Leave Hulk alone!'

   b   'No!'

   c   'No smash!'

▰▰▱ **18.** 'Get this man a shield!' Who says this about Steve Rogers?

   a   T'Challa

   b   Shuri

   c   Bucky Barnes

▰▱▱ **19.** At the end of Avengers: Infinity War, who are the only surviving Guardians of the Galaxy?

   a   Star-Lord and Groot

   b   Groot and Mantis

   c   Rocket and Nebula

20. What does Gamora make Star-Lord promise?

a   To kill her if she's ever captured by Thanos

b   To kill Thanos if he ever harms her

c   To destroy the Infinity Stones

21. What happens to Maria Hill and Nick Fury on the streets of New York?

a   They watch as everyone around them turns to dust

b   They are turned to dust

c   They are killed by the Nova Corps

22. At the end of *Avengers: Infinity War*, who does Nick Fury make his final plea for help to?

a   The Eternals

b   Captain Marvel

c   Iron Man

23. Name at least three surviving Avengers at the end of *Avengers: Infinity War*.

24. What is the name of Thor's new weapon?

a   Skullsplitter

b   Stonesmasher

c   Stormbreaker

25. Who forged Thor's new hammer?
a   The dwarf, Eitri
b   Tony Stark
c   His late father, Odin

26. Where was Thor's new hammer forged?
a   The Midgardian forge
b   The Nidavellir forge
c   The Nifleheim forge

27. From whose ship do Spider-Man and Iron Man rescue Doctor Strange?
a   Corvus Glaive's
b   Ebony Maw's
c   Thanos'

28. How many alternative realities did Doctor Strange see?
a   14,000,605
b   15,902,304
c   16,736,264

29. Out of the millions of alternative realities that Doctor Strange has seen, in how many of them were the Avengers victorious?
a   None
b   One
c   Three

30. Where do Wanda and Vision meet for their secret romance?
a   In Tokyo, Japan
b   In Berlin, Germany
c   In Edinburgh, Scotland

31. What do Pepper and Tony have planned in the coming months?
a   A press conference
b   Their wedding
c   The birth of their daughter

32. What are Ebony Maw, Cull Obsidian, Proxima Midnight and Corvus Glaive known as?
a   The Children of Thanos
b   The Nova Corps
c   The Anti-Avengers

33. Who crashes into the staircase in the middle of the Sanctum Sanctorum?
a   Thanos
b   Bruce Banner, aka Hulk
c   Thor

34. Why does Bruce Banner pilot the Hulkbuster armour?
- **a** Because he can't transform into Hulk
- **b** Because he's trying to suppress Hulk
- **c** Because it looks fun

35. What must Thor do to activate the forge of Nidavellir?
- **a** Destroy a sun
- **b** Summon lightning from a nearby planet
- **c** Reignite the core of a dying star

36. Where is Peter Parker when Thanos' emissaries arrive on Earth?
- **a** In class
- **b** Swinging through the streets of New York
- **c** On a school bus

37. How does Thanos manage to get hold of the Mind Stone, even though Wanda destroyed it?
- **a** By creating an identical copy using the Reality Stone
- **b** By going back in time using the Time Stone
- **c** By forcing Wanda to reverse its destruction

38. Where should Thor have hit Thanos with Stormbreaker?

a His heart
b His hand
c His head

39. In Wakanda, who does T'Challa ask to extract the Mind Stone from Vision's forehead?

a Bruce Banner
b Shuri, his sister
c Tony Stark

40. On which planet is the Soul Stone?

a Vormir
b Earth
c Xandar

41. 'Death follows him like a shadow.' Who says this about whom?

a Drax, about Thor
b Mantis, about Thanos
c Steve, about Tony

42. Which 'Children of Thanos' attack Wanda and Vision in Scotland?

a Proxima Midnight and Corvus Glaive
b Ebony Maw and Cull Obsidian
c Corvus Glaive and Cull Obsidian

43. Who is the guardian of the Soul Stone?

a The Nova Corps

b Doctor Strange

c The Stonekeeper

44. Which moon does Thanos come from?

a Titan

b Rhea

c Mimas

45. Who turns to dust in Tony Stark's arms?

a Pepper Potts

b Mantis

c Peter Parker, aka Spider-Man

ANT-MAN AND THE WASP

1. Which Super Hero's mother was lost in the Quantum Realm when they were a child?

a Ant-Man's

b The Wasp's

c Iron Man's

2. What is Hope Pym's mother's nickname for her?

a Peanut

b Butterfly

c Jellybean

3. What does Cassie shout when Luis interrupts her and Scott's game at the beginning of the film?

a 'It's a monster!'

b 'It's the fuzz!'

c 'It's Thanos!'

4. What does it say on the trophy that Cassie gives Scott?

a World's Best Dad

b World's Coolest Super Hero

c World's Greatest Grandma

5. What is the name of the client X-Con is trying to land a deal with?
a Karapetyan
b Goldstein
c Anderson

6. What colour was the wardrobe where Hope hid as a child?
a Red
b Blue
c Yellow

7. What was the name of the project that Hank Pym and Bill Foster worked on together?
a Project Titan
b Project Colossus
c Project Goliath

8. What does Scott tell Bill is the tallest he has ever got?
a 25 ft
b 65 ft
c 105 ft

9. What does Scott call the ant he uses to break into the building where Hank Pym's shrunken lab is being kept?
a Ulysses S. Gr-Ant
b Adam Ant
c Mark Ant-Tony

10. What gift does Bill Foster bring Ava Starr as a child?

   a   A doll

   b   A toy truck

   c   A teddy bear

11. What is Ava Starr's alias?

   a   Ghost

   b   Phantom

   c   Shadow

12. Which organisation built Ava's containment chamber?

   a   S.H.I.E.L.D.

   b   The FBI

   c   Stark Industries

13. What does Luis suggest his colleagues should have for breakfast, instead of pastries?

   a   Toast

   b   Pancakes

   c   Oatmeal packets

14. When under the influence of truth serum, where does Luis not tell Sonny Burch Scott is?

   a   In Hank's lab

   b   In a tricky spot, emotionally speaking

   c   In the woods

15. If Scott and Hope miss their chance, how long will it be before the probability fields align again?

a A decade

b A century

c A millennium

16. What does Luis tell Scott he hates about him?

a How he ties his shoes

b How he clicks his pen

c How he loads the dishwasher

17. What disguise does Hank wear to escape the FBI?

a An FBI agent's uniform

b A janitor's uniform

c A clown costume

18. In Scott's plan, what stage is 'fight Ghost'?

a 1b

b 2a

c 3c

19. What is the name of Ava Starr's father?
a   Victor
b   William
c   Elihas

20. Which creature nearly attacks Hank in the Quantum Realm?
a   Tardigrade
b   Ant
c   Dust mite

21. What colour is the toy car that Luis drives?
a   Purple
b   Red
c   Yellow

22. What weapon is Janet van Dyne carrying when Hank finds her in the Quantum Realm?
a   Sword
b   Bow
c   Batons

23. What additional crime does Sonny Burch admit to while under the influence of truth serum?
a   Health code violations
b   Tax fraud
c   Fashion crimes

24. What gift does Hank give Janet at the end of the film?

a A ring
b A teddy bear
c A house

25. What insect lands on Scott's car in the mini drive-through?

a Moth
b Beetle
c Wasp

CAPTAIN MARVEL

1. What colour is Kree blood?
a   Red
b   Blue
c   Gold

2. Who says the line 'I stared into the face of my mortal enemy and the face staring back was my own'?
a   Korath
b   Yon-Rogg
c   Talos

3. What shape-shifting species of alien are the Kree at war with?
a   Doppelgangers
b   Shifters
c   Skrulls

4. Who does the Supreme Intelligence take the form of in Vers' eyes?
a   Yon-Rogg
b   Dr. Wendy Lawson
c   Maria Rambeau

5. Where does Vers land when she first arrives on Earth?
a   A video store
b   A grocery store
c   An electronics store

6. What is the Kree name for Planet Earth?
a   C-53
b   D-42
c   F-91

7. What is the name of the bar that Carol used to visit when she was in the Air Force?
a   Skylar's Bar
b   Wingspan
c   Pancho's Bar

8. What does Nick Fury tell Vers she looks like in her flannel shirt?
a   Somebody's disaffected niece
b   A criminal
c   A teenage boy

9. What does Nick Fury use to bypass the Project Pegasus fingerprint security system?
a   A piece of tape
b   A paperclip
c   A ballpoint pen

10. What is the name of the creature that Fury and Vers find in the Air Force base?
a   Turkey
b   Goose
c   Eagle

11. What is on the baseball cap Nick Fury gives to Vers?

a   The S.W.O.R.D. logo

b   The S.H.I.E.L.D. logo

c   A cartoon of a cat

12. What does Vers do to prove to Maria and Monica that she's in Starforce?

a   Boils a kettle of water with her hands

b   Shoots a hole in the barn door

c   Cuts her arm to show her alien blood

13. What is Dr. Wendy Lawson's real name?

a   Vers

b   Talos

c   Mar-Vell

14. What is Carol's nickname for Monica Rambeau?

a   Captain Chaos

b   Lieutenant Trouble

c   Sergeant Danger

15. What is Vers' earliest memory of Hala?

a   A blood transfusion

b   An explosion

c   Seeing Yon-Rogg's face

16. What did Talos find in Mar-Vell's laboratory?
- **a** A cache of weapons
- **b** An Anulax battery
- **c** His family

17. What level of threat is Nick Fury categorised as by the Kree?
- **a** Low to none
- **b** Medium
- **c** High

18. What does Nick Fury say he's trusting Goose to do when he picks her up?
- **a** Kill the Kree
- **b** Not eat him
- **c** Drive the spaceship

19. How does Carol/Vers jokingly challenge Yon-Rogg to decide who gets the Tesseract?
- **a** Arm wrestling
- **b** Rock, paper, scissors
- **c** A foot race

20. True or false? The rest of Vers' Starforce team knew she was human all along.

21. How does the witness to Carol Danvers' crash landing on Earth describe her as dressed?

a 'In a spacesuit.'
b 'For laser tag.'
c 'For a wedding.'

22. Who says, 'I have nothing to prove to you'?

a Monica Rambeau, to her mother, Maria
b Nick Fury, to Carol Danvers
c Carol Danvers, to Yon-Rogg

23. What does Carol send Yon-Rogg home with?

a A message
b A black eye
c A fake Tesseract

24. How does Nick Fury's eye get damaged?

a Talos pokes him
b He gets scratched by Goose
c He falls down the stairs

25. Where does Carol tell Nick Fury to keep the Tesseract?

a On the Moon
b In another galaxy
c On Earth

26. What language are Dr. Wendy Lawson's notes written in?

a   English
b   Kree glyphs
c   Latin

27. Who helps Vers and Nick Fury escape from the Project Pegasus facility?

a   Phil Coulson
b   Korath
c   Maria Rambeau

28. How many years before the events of the film does Carol say her plane crashed?

a   Two
b   Six
c   Ten

29. What species is Goose?

a   Kree
b   Celestial
c   Flerken

30. What does Carol offer to do for Talos and his family?

a   Help them find a home
b   Find them a new identity on Earth
c   Make them dinner

AVENGERS: ENDGAME

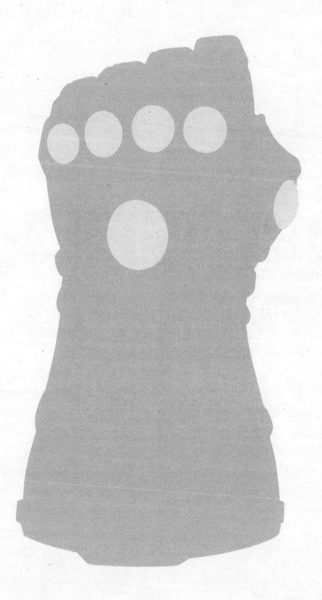

1. What nickname does Tony Stark give Nebula when they're stranded in space together?

a   The Angry Peacock

b   The Cerulean Toddler

c   The Blue Meanie

2. Who rescues Tony Stark and Nebula from space?

a   Captain Marvel

b   Thor

c   Captain America

3. What prompts Thor to say 'I like this one' about Captain Marvel?

a   She punches Captain America

b   She picks up Mjolnir

c   She doesn't flinch when his axe flies past her head

4. Who raises their hands when Rocket asks 'who here hasn't been to space'?

a   Tony Stark, Captain America and Black Widow

b   Black Widow, War Machine and Captain America

c   Thor, Black Widow and Tony Stark

5. True or False? Scott Lang's daughter Cassie was erased in the Blip.

6. What food does Hulk offer to Ant-Man?
a   A taco
b   A slice of pizza
c   Some fries

7. Where is New Asgard?
a   Scotland
b   Iceland
c   Norway

8. 'I think I liked you better either of the other ways.' Who says this to Hulk?
a   Valkyrie
b   Tony Stark
c   Natasha Romanoff

9. Who watches their family disappear in the Snap at the beginning of the film?
a   Iron Man
b   Hawkeye
c   Black Widow

10. Who says the words – 'see you in a minute' – before the Avengers travel back in time?
a   Black Widow
b   Captain America
c   Iron Man

11. After the Battle of New York, which Avenger is forced to take the stairs?

a Thor

b Iron Man

c Hulk

12. Who travels to Morag with Nebula to retrieve the Power Stone?

a Rocket

b James 'Rhodey' Rhodes, aka War Machine

c Clint Barton, aka Hawkeye

13. How does Captain America convince the S.H.I.E.L.D. agents to trust him after the Battle of New York?

a By whispering 'Hail Hydra'

b By performing a secret handshake

c By bribing them

14. What does Captain America tell his past self, surprising him for long enough to knock him out?

a 'Time travel is real.'

b 'Loki is escaping.'

c 'Bucky is alive.'

15. Who gives Bruce Banner/Hulk the Time Stone?

a The Ancient One

b Doctor Strange

c Wong

16. Who is the self-proclaimed 'wisest person in Asgard'?

a　Loki

b　Odin

c　Frigga

17. 'So he's an idiot.'
'Yeah.'
Who are Rhodey and Nebula talking about?

a　Iron Man

b　Star-Lord

c　Ant-Man

18. What do Steve and Tony steal from Camp Lehigh?

a　Pym Particles

b　The Space Stone

c　Super Soldier Serum

19. Which Infinity Stone is retrieved through Natasha Romanoff's sacrifice?

a　The Space Stone

b　The Time Stone

c　The Soul Stone

20. Which Avenger dons the new Infinity Gauntlet to perform the first reverse snap?

a　Iron Man

b　Thor

c　Hulk

21. How does Thor respond to Captain America wielding Mjolnir?

a   'I knew it.'

b   'I don't understand.'

c   'Put that down!'

22. Who is the first person to emerge from the portals in the final battle?

a   Black Panther

b   Falcon

c   Spider-Man

23. What is Tony Stark's response to Thanos saying 'I am inevitable'?

a   'No you're not.'

b   'I am Iron Man.'

c   'Nothing is inevitable.'

24. Who becomes King of Asgard?

a   Thor

b   Valkyrie

c   Loki

25. Where do we last see Captain America?

a   Dancing with Peggy Carter

b   Fighting Hydra

c   Sitting on a bench with Sam

26. Who kills Thanos the first time round?

a   Captain Marvel

b   Iron Man

c   Thor

27. Who travels to the Battle of New York to retrieve the Tesseract?

a   Black Widow, Hawkeye, Captain America and Iron Man

b   Ant-Man, Captain America and Iron Man

c   Hulk, Black Widow, Ant-Man and Hawkeye

28. Who accompanies Thor back to Asgard to retrieve the Aether?

a   Rocket

b   Nebula

c   Valkyrie

29. Who escapes from the Battle of New York with the Tesseract?

a   Loki

b   Brock Rumlow

c   Captain America

30. What does Sam Wilson say in Captain America's earpiece after the Blip as a portal opens?

a   'We're back.'

b   'Are you ok?'

c   'On your left.'

BLACK WIDOW

1. What colour is young Natasha's hair?
   a   Red
   b   Blonde
   c   Blue

2. How does young Yelena respond when Melina tells her they're going home?
   a   'We just left home.'
   b   'We don't have a home.'
   c   'Where is home?'

3. How old was Yelena when she was sent to the Red Room?
   a   6
   b   9
   c   12

4. What does Thaddeus Ross call Ant-Man?
   a   Tiny Man
   b   The Incredible Shrinking Convict
   c   That Bug Guy

5. Natasha Romanoff and which other Avenger remain on the run after the events of *Captain America: Civil War*?
   a   Tony Stark, aka Iron Man
   b   Clint Barton, aka Hawkeye
   c   Steve Rogers, aka Captain America

6. Who attacks Natasha as she is driving in Norway?

a Yelena

b Alexei

c Taskmaster

7. What does Natasha use to subdue Yelena when they fight in her Budapest apartment?

a A net curtain

b A china plate

c A bottle of soda

8. What did Natasha believe she had accomplished as her final step in defecting from the Red Room to S.H.I.E.L.D.?

a Befriending Clint Barton

b Taking the synthetic gas that targets the Red Room's mind control

c Killing General Dreykov

9. What aspect of Natasha's fighting does Yelena make fun of?

a Her unwillingness to kill

b The way she poses

c Her precision

10. What job does Natasha have in Yelena's fantasy life?

a Science teacher

b Accountant

c ER doctor

11. What does Rick Mason give Yelena and Natasha when they ask him for a jet?

a The S.H.I.E.L.D. helicarrier

b A white van

c A helicopter

12. What do Yelena and Natasha hide their communication device in when breaking Alexei out of prison?

a A Red Guardian action figure

b A piece of bread

c A Captain America lunchbox

13. 'I swear if I hear one more word from him I will kick him in the face.' Who says this about whom?

a Natasha about Dreykov

b Yelena about Alexei

c Melina about Alexei

14. What type of animal does Melina keep on her farm?

a Pigs

b Chickens

c Cows

15. What is in the photo album that Melina shows to Natasha?

a Pictures of Natasha's birth parents

b Pictures of Melina's own childhood

c Pictures of the years they spent as a family

16. Where is the Red Room?
- **a** Deep underground
- **b** On Melina's farm
- **c** In an aerial facility

17. In order to infiltrate the Red Room, who swaps faces with whom?
- **a** Yelena with Natasha
- **b** Melina with Natasha
- **c** Yelena with Alexei

18. Who is Taskmaster?
- **a** Melina
- **b** Antonia Dreykov
- **c** Rick Mason

19. What does Yelena say in response to mimicking Natasha's three-point-landing pose?
- **a** 'This is actually pretty cool.'
- **b** 'I see why she likes this.'
- **c** 'That was disgusting.'

20. What, according to Dreykov, is the only resource that the world has too much of?
- **a** Heroes
- **b** Girls
- **c** Idiots

21. What does Natasha do to combat the pheromonal lock that prevents her from harming Dreykov?

a Breaks her own nose to sever a nerve

b Holds her breath so she can't smell him

c Sprays him with perfume

22. Where do Yelena, Natasha, Alexei and Melina live while they masquerade as a family?

a Indiana

b Kentucky

c Ohio

23. What is Natasha's response to the other Widows asking what to do now?

a 'Whatever you like.'

b 'Take down Dreykov.'

c 'Get as far away from here as possible.'

24. What does Yelena give Natasha before they part?

a The Widow antidote

b Her vest

c A photograph of themselves as children

25. In the mid-credits scene, who does Contessa Valentina Allegra de Fontaine blame for Natasha's death?

a Clint Barton, aka Hawkeye

b Tony Stark, aka Iron Man

c Thanos

26. In which city are Yelena and Natasha reunited for the first time in their adult lives?

a Helsinki
b Budapest
c Krakov

27. What is Taskmaster's special skill?

a Mimicking whoever she's fighting
b Not feeling any pain
c Immunity to poison

28. When Yelena tells Natasha that if Dreykov kills her, then one of the big ones will come to avenge her, which Avenger does she reference?

a '... the man with the ants.'
b '... the one with the shield.'
c '... the god from space.'

29. 'Did he talk to you about me?' Who is Alexei referring to?

a Captain America
b Thor
c Iron Man

30. What does Natasha say to Dreykov after he tells her his plan?

a 'That will never work.'
b 'Thank you for your cooperation.'
c 'You're a monster.'

SHANG-CHI AND THE LEGEND OF THE TEN RINGS

SHANG-CHI
AND THE LEGEND OF THE TEN RINGS

1. What hidden village is Wenwu searching for when he meets Li?

  a   Xitang

  b   Ta Lo

  c   Xinle

2. What zhezhi creature does Shang-Chi's mother give him as a child?

  a   A dragon

  b   A tiger

  c   A snake

3. What is Shang-Chi's job at the beginning of the film?

  a   Waiter

  b   Parking valet

  c   Chauffeur

4. What job does Katy do after graduating from college?

  a   Shop assistant

  b   Bar tender

  c   Hotel valet

5. How does Katy help Shang-Chi when he is attacked on the bus?

  a   She punches one of his attackers

  b   She calls the police

  c   She drives the bus when the bus driver is knocked unconscious

6. How old was Shang-Chi when he ran away to San Francisco?

a 14

b 18

c 21

7. What is the name of Xialing's fight club?

a The Red Dragon Club

b The Golden Daggers Club

c The Ten Rings Club

8. Who does Katy bet on when Xialing and Shang-Chi fight?

a Shang-Chi

b Xialing

c She doesn't bet

9. How does Katy distract the Ten Rings member who attacks her outside Xialing's fight club?

a She sings

b She dances

c She screams

10. What does Razor Fist take from Shang-Chi after the fight on the bus?

a His watch

b His phone

c A pendant

11. What advice does Xialing give Katy when facing Wenwu?

    a   'Don't let him know you're scared of him.'

    b   'Just nod. Don't talk. He'll forget you're there.'

    c   'Make eye contact and answer his questions.'

12. Which English city is Trevor Slattery from?

    a   London

    b   Liverpool

    c   Manchester

13. Whose car do Shang-Chi, Xialing, Katy and Trevor steal from Wenwu's garage?

    a   Razor Fist's

    b   Wenwu's

    c   Ying Nan's

14. What does Wenwu call Katy?

    a   Trouble

    b   Outsider

    c   American Girl

15. How is Ying Nan related to Shang-Chi?

    a   She is his mother

    b   She is his aunt

    c   She is his half-sister

16. What was the name of the legendary creature which saved Ta Lo from the Dweller-in-Darkness?

a   The Great Protector

b   The Dragon Guardian

c   The Champion of Light

17. What is Wenwu's order to his men on arriving at Ta Lo?

a   'Kill them all.'

b   'Find my wife.'

c   'Burn it down.'

18. What happens when Wenwu breaches the Dark Gate?

a - Some soul-eaters escape

b   Li returns to life

c   Wenwu loses his power

19. What weapon does Katy learn to fight with?

a   A whip

b   A sword

c   A bow and arrow

20. True or false? Trevor Slattery is killed in the battle with the soul-eaters.

21. What colour are The Ten Rings when Shang-Chi uses them?
- **a** Blue
- **b** Gold
- **c** Green

22. Who does Wenwu believe is calling to him from beyond the Dark Gate?
- **a** The Dweller-in-Darkness
- **b** His mother
- **c** His wife, Li

23. 'I'm not leaving you again.' Who does Shang-Chi say these words to?
- **a** Katy
- **b** His father, Wenwu
- **c** His sister, Xialing

24. Which two Avengers study The Ten Rings in Wong's library?
- **a** Doctor Strange and T'Challa
- **b** Bruce Banner and Captain Marvel
- **c** Thor and Star-Lord

25. Where do Katy and Shang-Chi take Wong in the mid-credits scene?
- **a** A karaoke bar
- **b** A shawarma restaurant
- **c** Xialing's fight club

26. What were Xialing's and Shang-Chi's jade pendants the key to?

a The Dark Gate

b A map to Ta Lo

c A box holding The Ten Rings

27. What Shakespeare play did Trevor Slattery perform a monologue from to stop Wenwu from killing him?

a *Macbeth*

b *Hamlet*

c *King Lear*

28. True or false? Shang-Chi's mother is being held captive in Ta Lo.

29. Who saves Razor Fist from a soul-eater?

a Xialing

b Ying Nan

c Katy

30. What shape does the Great Protector take?

a A dragon

b A serpent

c A human

ETERNALS

1. What planet are the Eternals from?
a   Earth
b   Morag
c   Olympia

2. Where does Sersi work?
a   A museum
b   A school
c   An archeological site

3. What gift does Sersi give Dane for his birthday?
a   An ancient sword
b   A handmade scarf
c   A ring with his family crest

4. What is Sersi's instruction to Sprite when they are attacked by the Deviant Kro on the streets of London?
a   'Keep Dane safe.'
b   'Come with me.'
c   'Help me kill it.'

5. What is Sprite's main power?
a   She can shapeshift
b   She can project lifelike illusions
c   She can fly

6. Who is the Prime Eternal at the beginning of the film?

a   Ajak

b   Ikaris

c   Phastos

7. Where does Sersi live in the present day?

a   New York

b   London

c   Paris

8. What invention, created by Phastos, is dismissed by the other Eternals as 'too advanced' for humanity?

a   The plough

b   The internet

c   The steam engine

9. What do Sersi, Ikaris and Sprite find when they go to the home of their leader, Ajak?

a   She has disappeared

b   She has been killed

c   She has turned into a Deviant

10. What is Kingo's job when the other Eternals find him on Earth?

a   A Bollywood actor

b   A Hollywood stuntman

c   A college professor

11. Who does Ikaris joke should lead the Avengers?
- **a** Ant-Man
- **b** Vision
- **c** Himself

12. Which Avenger does Kingo say won't return his calls?
- **a** Thor
- **b** Captain Marvel
- **c** Iron Man

13. What does Dane think Sersi is?
- **a** An alien
- **b** A wizard
- **c** A con artist

14. What is Karun to Kingo?
- **a** His bodyguard
- **b** His valet
- **c** His father

15. Which Eternal is killed by Kro?
- **a** Thena
- **b** Kingo
- **c** Gilgamesh

▰▰▰ 16. 'Without their flaws, they wouldn't be human.' Who says this?

a   Druig
b   Ikaris
c   Phastos

▰▰▰ 17. In which ancient empire are Sersi and Ikaris married?

a   The Incan Empire
b   Imperial Rome
c   The Gupta Empire

▰▰▱ 18. What illness does Thena have?

a   Dementia
b   Mahd Wy'ry
c   Aphasia

▰▰▰ 19. Why did Kingo leave Sprite in Macedonia?

a   Because Sprite was too mischievous
b   Because he'd fallen in love
c   Because he was sick of moving whenever people noticed Sprite didn't age

▰▰▱ 20. True or false? Sprite chooses to stay with the other Eternals when Ikaris leaves.

21. What does Kingo suggest as an alternative name to the Uni-Mind?
a   Brainstorm
b   We-ternal
c   Super-Brain

22. 'You've never had to fight me.'
'But I've always wanted to.'
Which two characters are speaking here?
a   Sersi and Sprite
b   Druig and Phastos
c   Thena and Ikaris

23. Who does Sprite create an illusion of to distract Sersi?
a   Ajak
b   Ikaris
c   Druig

24. What does Sersi do for Sprite at the end of the movie?
a   Makes her appear older
b   Allows her to leave Earth
c   Removes her immortality and makes her human

25. Which animal does Dane jokingly ask Sersi to change him into?
a   A lion
b   A giraffe
c   An eagle

26. What does Gilgamesh's apron say?
   a 'Kiss the cook'
   b 'Stay out of the kitchen'
   c 'Barbeque king'

27. What is Druig's power?
   a He can fly
   b He can manipulate the elements
   c He can manipulate the minds of others

28. What does Phastos tell his husband Sersi and Ikaris are called?
   a Sylvia and Isaac
   b Sarah and Iain
   c Sally and Ivan

29. How does Ikaris kill Ajak?
   a He disintegrates her with his eye beams
   b He allows her to be killed by Deviants
   c He allows her to drown

30. Where does Ikaris fly in atonement for his crimes?
   a The Sun
   b A black hole
   c Into a volcano

DOCTOR STRANGE IN THE MULTIVERSE OF MADNESS

DOCTOR STRANGE
IN THE MULTIVERSE OF MADNESS

1. Who does Doctor Strange dream of in the opening moments of the film?
a Wong
b The Scarlet Witch
c America Chavez

2. Whose wedding is interrupted by a demon attacking America Chavez?
a Dr. Christine Palmer's
b Dr. Nicodemus West's
c Karl Mordo's

3. Who does Dr. West say he lost while he was gone during the Blip?
a His cats and his brother
b Both his parents
c His goldfish and his girlfriend

4. How does Doctor Strange kill Gargantos as it attacks America Chavez?
a He traps it in a portal
b He impales it with a lamp post
c He crushes it with a bus

5. What is America Chavez's main superpower?

a   She can Dreamwalk

b   She can predict the future

c   She can travel through the Multiverse

6. What recurring nightmare does Wong realise is happening in another universe?

a   Running naked from a clown

b   Riding on the back of a giant spider

c   His mother trying to eat him

7. When we first see Wanda, she is dreaming of her children. What is she doing with them?

a   Playing catch in the backyard

b   Eating ice cream in the park

c   Baking with them

8. When Doctor Strange visits Wanda, what makes him realise that she has been responsible for the attacks on America Chavez?

a   She knows America's name

b   He notices the Hex around her orchard

c   She has blood on her shirt

9. What ancient custom does Wong remind Doctor Strange about?
a Wearing sorcerer's robes
b Bowing to the Sorcerer Supreme
c Going on pilgrimages to Kamar-Taj

10. What instruction does The Scarlet Witch whisper to the sorcerers defending Kamar-Taj?
a 'Run.'
b 'Hide.'
c 'Attack.'

11. What is America's first rule of Multiversal travel?
a Find food
b Don't talk to yourself
c You don't know anything

12. How many universes, including 838, has America been to?
a 51
b 73
c 206

13. Who does America see on Memory Lane?
a Doctor Strange
b Her sister
c Her mothers

■□□ **14.** Who is the master of the New York Sanctum in Earth 838?

a Stephen Strange

b Karl Mordo

c Wong

■■□ **15.** After saying 'I always expected this day would come...', how does 838-Mordo first react to seeing Doctor Strange?

a He attacks him

b He hugs him

c He screams

■■■ **16.** What drugged drink does 838-Mordo give Doctor Strange and America?

a Tea

b Coffee

c Apple juice

■■□ **17.** What designation is Doctor Strange's universe?

a 1

b 801

c 616

■□□ **18.** What colour is 838-Christine's hair?

a Blonde

b Red

c Black

◢◢◪ **19.** What Super Hero organisation runs Earth 838?

a   Hydra

b   S.H.I.E.L.D.

c   The Illuminati

◢◪◪ **20.** Who is The First Avenger in Earth 838?

a   Steve Rogers

b   Peggy Carter

c   Sam Wilson

◢◢◢ **21.** Who killed 838-Doctor Strange?

a   Black Bolt

b   Professor Charles Xavier

c   Thanos

◢◢◢ **22.** What was the name of Doctor Strange's sister?

a   Katie

b   Emma

c   Donna

◢◪◪ **23.** What does Doctor Strange possess to Dreamwalk into his own universe?

a   His own dead body

b   A mannequin

c   Wong

24. True or False? Wong tells Doctor Strange to take America's power to stop The Scarlet Witch.

25. What appears on Doctor Strange's forehead at the end of the film?
a   Rotting skin
b   A tentacle
c   An eye

WANDAVISION

EPISODE 1: FILMED BEFORE A LIVE STUDIO AUDIENCE

1. What is Agnes' excuse for not coming to greet her new neighbour sooner?
- **a** She was at a PTA meeting
- **b** Her mother-in-law was in town
- **c** The Chitauri were trying to invade Earth

2. How much has the productivity of the company where Vision works increased since his arrival?
- **a** 300%
- **b** 1,000%
- **c** 25%

3. For which appliance is there an ad in the middle of the episode?
- **a** Toaster
- **b** Iron
- **c** Rocket launcher

4. What does Vision play to keep the Harts busy before dinner?
- **a** Trombone
- **b** Banjo
- **c** Ukulele

5. What is the knocker on the door of the house replaced by when the Harts leave?

a   A lobster

b   A parrot

c   A replica of Mjolnir

6. At the very end of this episode, which organisation's logo can be seen?

a   S.W.O.R.D.

b   S.H.I.E.L.D.

c   Hydra

EPISODE 2: DON'T TOUCH THAT DIAL

1. Which local group does Vision decide to join?

a   Neighbourhood Watch

b   Bridge club

c   Stamp society

2. Wanda finds a colourful toy in her hedge. What is it?

a   A fire truck

b   A Captain America figurine

c   A helicopter

3. What disrupts Vision's internal system?

a   An electric shock

b   A glass of whiskey

c   Chewing gum

4. What act are Wanda and Vision performing at the talent show?

a   Trapeze
b   Magic
c   Dancing

5. Who comes out of a manhole at the end of the episode?

a   A S.W.O.R.D. agent
b   Minutemen
c   An Ultron drone

6. What is the name of the head of the neighbourhood?

a   Agnes
b   Dottie
c   Geraldine

EPISODE 3: NOW IN COLOR

1. What is the name of the doctor who is monitoring Wanda's pregnancy?

a   Dr. Banner
b   Dr. Nielson
c   Dr. Strange

2. Where does Wanda's doctor intend to go on holiday?

a   Paris
b   Sokovia
c   Bermuda

3. What is Herb, Vision's neighbour, pruning instead of his hedge?

a   His fence
b   His wall
c   His car

4. What does Wanda cause when she has contractions?

a   A flood
b   A hurricane
c   A blackout

5. What animal shows up in Wanda's house during her pregnancy?

a   A stork
b   A giraffe
c   Alligator Loki

6. What are the names of Wanda and Vision's twins?

a   Stan and Jack
b   Steve and Tony
c   Billy and Tommy

EPISODE 4: WE INTERRUPT THIS PROGRAM

1. Who is Monica Rambeau?

a   A S.W.O.R.D. agent
b   The mayor of Westview
c   A widow

2. In which state is the city of Westview located?
a   New Jersey
b   California
c   Kansas

3. What does Dr. Darcy Lewis use to solve the mystery of Westview?
a   A satellite dish
b   A television set
c   The Tesseract

4. What superpower does Wanda's brother Pietro have?
a   Super speed
b   Invisibility
c   Immortality

5. Where does Monica reappear when she returns from the Blip?
a   S.W.O.R.D. headquarters
b   Space
c   A hospital

6. What makes Wanda turn on Monica?
a   Monica calls Wanda a witch
b   Monica mentions Ultron
c   Monica sees Wanda use her powers

7. What does the S.W.O.R.D. agent get turned into when he crosses the Hex?

a A beekeeper
b A fencer
c A scuba diver

EPISODE 5: ON A VERY SPECIAL EPISODE...

1. What is the name of the force field that surrounds Westview?

a The Palisade
b The Scarlet Shield
c The Hex

2. What is the name of Vision's office mate?

a Norm
b Dwight
c Homer

3. What is the name of the dog adopted by Wanda's sons?

a Mandrake
b Sparky
c Lucky the Pizza Dog

4. What does Vision read to Billy to try to get him to sleep?

a Charles Darwin
b The Phone Book
c The Darkhold

EPISODE 6: ALL-NEW HALLOWEEN SPOOKTACULAR!

1. What holiday is the city of Westview preparing to celebrate at the beginning of this episode?
a Christmas
b Halloween
c Thanksgiving

2. Tommy, one of Wanda and Vision's twins, has the same powers as another character. Who?
a Pietro
b Hulk
c Clint

3. Using the waves emitted by which artefact enables Hayward to monitor Vision?
a His Infinity Stone
b His battery
c His vibranium

4. What does Wanda transform the military camp on the outskirts of Westview into?
a A live-action role-playing game
b A circus
c A festival

EPISODE 7: BREAKING THE FOURTH WALL

1. What does S.W.O.R.D. use to break the barrier around Westview?
- **a** A space rover
- **b** A tank
- **c** A helicopter

2. Who is Agnes really?
- **a** A Hydra agent
- **b** A Skrull
- **c** A witch

3. What is Agnes' real name?
- **a** Carol Danvers
- **b** Darcy Lewis
- **c** Agatha Harkness

4. What is the title of the sitcom revealing Agnes' actions?
- **a** *Agatha All Along*
- **b** *Sacred Agatha*
- **c** *My Beloved Agatha*

5. Which product is advertised in the Nexus commercial?
- **a** Toothpaste
- **b** Shampoo
- **c** An antidepressant

EPISODE 8: PREVIOUSLY ON

1. What does Agnes/Agatha use to protect herself from Wanda?
a A force field
b Runes
c Illusions

2. What does Agatha use to explore Wanda's past?
a Her photo album
b A strand of her hair
c A family jewel

3. What colour is the Vision rebooted by S.W.O.R.D.?
a Gold
b Black
c White

EPISODE 9: THE SERIES FINALE

1. Where does Agatha Harkness get her power?
a In the flow of the Multiverse
b In the Dark Dimension
c From the other witches

■■◻ **2.** How does Agatha describe the Darkhold to Wanda?
- **a** The Book of Dark Magic
- **b** The Book of the Damned
- **c** The Book of Prophecy

■■■ **3.** What is the real name of the fake Pietro?
- **a** Ralph Bohner
- **b** Scott Lang
- **c** John Walker

■◻◻ **4.** What does Agatha tell Wanda she will become?
- **a** The Sorcerer Supreme
- **b** The Avatar of Khonshu
- **c** The Scarlet Witch

LOKI

EPISODE 1: GLORIOUS PURPOSE

1. In what year does the first scene of the first episode take place?
a   2012
b   2022
c   2099

2. What is the name of the TVA mascot?
a   Miss Second
b   Chronoboy
c   Miss Minutes

3. Mobius, in his first appearance, investigates a church in 1549. In which city is it located?
a   Aix-la-Chapelle
b   Aix-en-Provence
c   Aix-les-Bains

4. Loki witnesses his own death. Who kills him?
a   Thanos
b   Ultron
c   Hela

5. What are the TVA soldiers called?
a   The Minute Eaters
b   Minutemen
c   Stormtimers

6. What does TVA stand for?
  a   Time Variance Authority
  b   Temple of Anarchic Variations
  c   Tribe of Ancient Values

EPISODE 2: THE VARIANT

1. Which hunter is captured by a variant while tracking Loki?
  a   C-20
  b   B-52
  c   I-45

2. In what place do the TVA pursue the 'hooded Loki'?
  a   A rock concert
  b   A circus show
  c   A medieval festival

3. The variant Loki gave a child a futuristic product of the brand 'Kablooie'. What was it?
  a   An energy drink
  b   Chewing gum
  c   A trading card game

4. What is the name of the store destroyed in Haven Hills, Alabama?
  a   Roxxcart Super Market
  b   Cartroxx Super Market
  c   Calorox Super Market

■□□ **5.** What is the rank of Ravonna Renslayer, Mobius' superior?

a　Commissioner

b　Captain

c　Judge

EPISODE 3: LAMENTIS

■□□ **1.** Where has the Loki variant hidden from the TVA?

a　In the apocalypses

b　In big parties

c　In the Big Bangs

■■□ **2.** What are the names of the leaders of the TVA?

a　Guardians of the Galaxy

b　Time Masters

c　Time Keepers

■□□ **3.** What name has the Loki variant given herself?

a　Lokiette

b　She-Loki

c　Sylvie

4. What is Lamentis 1?
a   The severed head of a Celestial
b   A moon
c   A living planet

5. With what device do the TVA travel through the time stream?
a   A TemPad
b   A cell phone
c   A Strucker watch

6. What is the name of the ship in charge of evacuating the privileged people from Lamentis 1?
a   The *Statesman*
b   The *Ark*
c   The *Milano*

7. What do the Lokis eventually discover about the TVA members?
a   They are variants
b   They are super soldiers
c   They are androids

8. During their first meeting, with which weapon does Loki confront Sylvie?
  a   A war hammer
  b   A spear
  c   Two daggers

EPISODE 4: THE NEXUS EVENT

1. What was Sylvie doing when the Minutemen arrested her?
  a   Turning herself into a snake
  b   Playing with figurines
  c   Enchanting Odin

2. Caught in a time loop, from whom does Loki suffer the wrath of multiple times?
  a   Odin
  b   Volstagg
  c   Lady Sif

3. What is the weapon of choice for the Minutemen?
  a   The time gauntlet
  b   A Time Stick
  c   A Chronogun

4. One of the Loki variants is an animal.
What animal?

a   A frog

b   A goat

c   An alligator

5. What do the Time Keepers turn out to be?

a   Androids

b   Variants

c   S.W.O.R.D. agents

6. When Loki wakes up, he is faced with several variants of himself. How many of them are there?

a   10

b   7

c   4

7. When Sylvie faces one of the Time Keepers, what weapon does she use?

a   A bow and arrow

b   A sword

c   An axe

8. What does Renslayer tell Sylvie about her Nexus Event?

a   Sylvie summoned Mjolnir

b   She doesn't remember

c   The information is classified

9. What did Sylvie steal from the TVA as a child?

a   A Time Stick

b   Miss Minutes

c   A TemPad

EPISODE 5: JOURNEY INTO MYSTERY

1. What happens to the variants pruned by the TVA?

a   They are killed

b   They are sent back in time

c   They are sent to the Void

2. What colour is Alioth – the living tempest in the Void?

a   Purple

b   Green

c   Orange

■■◻ **3.** Who did Kid Loki kill?
  a   Thor
  b   Odin
  c   Frigga

■■◻ **4.** Who does Boastful Loki claim to have defeated?
  a   Thor and Odin
  b   Hela and Surtur
  c   Captain America and Iron Man

■◻◻ **5.** Which other variant does Loki end up running into?
  a   General Loki
  b   President Loki
  c   King Loki

■◻◻ **6.** What vehicle does Mobius use in the Void to save Loki and Sylvie?
  a   A car
  b   A helicopter
  c   A hang glider

■◻◻ **7.** Which variant sacrifices himself to divert Alioth's attention?
  a   Kid Loki
  b   Alligator Loki
  c   Classic Loki

8. Which Thor variant do we see in the Void?
   a   Frog Thor
   b   Alligator Thor
   c   Only Child Thor

9. What does Classic Loki claim is a Loki's role?
   a   The God of Revenge
   b   The God of Mischief
   c   The God of Outcasts

EPISODE 6: FOR ALL TIME. ALWAYS.

1. What is the name of the inhabitant of the Citadel?
   a   He Who Is
   b   He Who Remains
   c   He Who Knows

2. Where is the Citadel located?
   a   At the end of time
   b   At the dawn of time
   c   Outside of time

3. Who welcomes Loki and Sylvie in the Citadel?
   a   Mobius
   b   Judge Renslayer
   c   Miss Minutes

4. What is He Who Remains holding in his hand when he first appears in Episode 6?
- **a** A Time Stick
- **b** A TemPad
- **c** An apple

5. What was Judge Renslayer before she worked for the TVA?
- **a** A Supreme Court Justice
- **b** An educator
- **c** A comic book writer

6. Where does Judge Renslayer say she is going when she leaves the TVA?
- **a** To the Citadel
- **b** In search of free will
- **c** To find Miss Minutes

THE FALCON AND THE WINTER SOLDIER

THE FALCON AND
THE WINTER SOLDIER

EPISODE 1: NEW WORLD ORDER

1. What is the first object to appear on screen in Episode 1?
- **a** Captain America's shield
- **b** The Winter Soldier's jacket
- **c** An iron

2. What is the name of the organisation that wants to abolish nations?
- **a** The Flag Smashers
- **b** The Children of Thanos
- **c** AIM

3. What is the name of Falcon's drone?
- **a** Blue Bird
- **b** Black Hawk
- **c** Redwing

4. On the internet, where do the conspiracists think Steve Rogers is?
- **a** On Mars
- **b** On the Moon
- **c** In the Dark Dimension

5. Who tries to convince Sam Wilson to keep Captain America's shield?
- **a** Black Widow
- **b** Captain Marvel
- **c** War Machine

▰▰▰ 6. What is being broadcast on TV when Bucky wakes up from his nightmare?

a A reality show
b A game show
c A football match

▰▰▰ 7. In which state do Sam Wilson's sister and her children live?

a Louisiana
b Alabama
c Pennsylvania

▰▰▱ 8. What is the name of the fishing boat owned by the Wilson family?

a The *Pequod*
b The *Stan & Jack*
c The *Paul & Darlene*

▰▰▱ 9. What is the name of Sam's home town in Louisiana?

a Lafayette
b Baton Rouge
c Delacroix

THE FALCON AND THE WINTER SOLDIER

EPISODE 2: THE STAR-SPANGLED MAN

1. At what event does John Walker's induction as the new Captain America take place?
  a At a political meeting
  b At a hip-hop concert
  c At a pep rally

2. In which European city does Falcon use his drone to spot the Flag Smashers?
  a Rome
  b Munich
  c Paris

3. What is the Flag Smashers' motto?
  a 'Thanos was right'
  b 'Redraw the map'
  c 'One world, one people'

4. Who is the partner of John Walker, the new Captain America?
  a Battlestar
  b Shatterstar
  c Redwing

5. How many super soldiers do Sam and Bucky encounter during the fight on the trucks?
  a 8
  b 60
  c 4

6. By which mysterious character's men are the Flag Smashers attacked?
- **a** Power Broker
- **b** Kingpin
- **c** Iron Monger

7. For what reason is Bucky arrested?
- **a** He hasn't paid his parking tickets
- **b** He has a book overdue at the library from 1944
- **c** He missed his therapy sessions

8. Falcon and the Winter Soldier seek the help of a criminal. Who?
- **a** Loki
- **b** Baron Zemo
- **c** Thanos

EPISODE 3: POWER BROKER

1. Where is Baron Zemo imprisoned?
- **a** On the Raft
- **b** At Alcatraz
- **c** In Berlin

2. What identity does Sam take on when undercover in Madripoor?
- **a** Smiling Tiger
- **b** White Tiger
- **c** Wilson Fisk

3. Which ex-S.H.I.E.L.D. agent do Sam and Bucky meet in Madripoor?

a Phil Coulson

b Sharon Carter

c Nick Fury

4. By what means of transport does Baron Zemo travel?

a An airship

b A private jet

c A flying saucer

5. Which member of the Dora Milaje appears at the end of this episode, searching for Baron Zemo?

a Okoye

b Ayo

c Xoliswa

EPISODE 4: THE WHOLE WORLD IS WATCHING

1. Which of these three words is not part of the Winter Soldier's activation code?

a Shrimp

b Benign

c Rusted

2. Where do the Flag Smashers hide the doses of the Super Soldier Serum?

a   In a cemetery

b   In a cinema

c   In a church

3. Why does Baron Zemo want to obtain the doses of Super Soldier Serum?

a   To sell them

b   To inject them

c   To destroy them

4. By whom is the last vial of Super Soldier Serum stolen?

a   By Baron Zemo

b   By Sam Wilson

c   By John Walker

◢◻◻ 5. John Walker kills a Flag Smasher to avenge:
   a   Battlestar
   b   Vision
   c   Steve Rogers

◢◻◻ 6. With which weapon does John Walker kill a Flag Smasher in combat?
   a   With a repulsor beam
   b   With a samurai sword
   c   With Captain America's shield

◢◢◢ 7. What is the last name of Karli, the leader of the Flag Smashers?
   a   Romanoff
   b   Maximoff
   c   Morgenthau

EPISODE 5: TRUTH

◢◢◢ 1. What is the name of the Flag Smasher murdered by John Walker?
   a   Bruce
   b   Steve
   c   Nico

◢◢◻ 2. What title does Valentina Allegra de Fontaine have?
   a   Contessa
   b   Marquise
   c   Baroness

3. What is the name of the maximum security prison where the Dora Milaje take Baron Zemo?

a   The Vault

b   The Raft

c   The Kyln

4. What is Bucky helping Sam and his sister fix?

a   Their house

b   Their family boat

c   Their motorhome

5. What language does Batroc speak?

a   French

b   German

c   Greek

6. Where does the briefcase that Bucky gives to Sam come from?

a   Wakanda

b   Asgard

c   New York

7. What is Batroc's first name?

a   Fred

b   Georges

c   Louis

EPISODE 6: ONE WORLD, ONE PEOPLE

1. What was in the briefcase that Bucky gave to Sam?
a   A suit
b   A shield
c   A drone

2. What Super Hero mantle does Sam take on?
a   Battlestar
b   Nomad
c   Captain America

3. John Walker is no longer Captain America. What name does he choose to wear?
a   U.S.Agent
b   The Captain
c   The New Avenger

4. What is the real identity of the Power Broker?
a   Sharon Carter
b   Baron Zemo
c   Contessa Valentina Allegra de Fontaine

5. Of which Avenger were Sam Wilson and Bucky Barnes both loyal friends?

a Steve Rogers

b Scott Lang

c Wanda Maximoff

6. What French expression does Batroc use when he sees Sam?

a 'A bird in the hand is worth two in the bush.'

b 'So much goes into the water that in the end it breaks.'

c 'The robes don't make the monk.'

MARVEL
WHAT IF...?

EPISODE 1: WHAT IF... CAPTAIN CARTER WERE THE FIRST AVENGER?

1. What is the name of the guide who observes the different realities?
a The Watcher
b Thanos
c The Guardian

2. What colour is the Super Soldier Serum that turns Peggy into Captain Carter?
a Blue
b Yellow
c Green

3. In which part of New York City was Steve Rogers born and raised?
a Queens
b Brooklyn
c The Bronx

4. Before becoming Captain Carter, Peggy Carter was:
a Agent Carter
b Professor Carter
c Lieutenant Carter

5. What is the name of the scientist who invented the Super Soldier Serum?

a   Howard Stark

b   Hank Pym

c   Abraham Erskine

6. In which country does Hydra find the Tesseract, the jewel of Odin's treasure room?

a   Norway

b   France

c   Canada

7. Which regiment does Captain Carter free from enemy territory?

a   The 105th

b   The 107th

c   The 112th

8. On what day does Peggy owe Steve Rogers a dance?

a   Friday night

b   Saturday night

c   Sunday night

9. What does Steve Rogers find after Peggy fights off the giant octopus?

a   The Tesseract

b   Captain Carter's shield

c   Super Soldier Serum

EPISODE 2: WHAT IF... T'CHALLA BECAME A STAR-LORD?

1. What is the name of the planet where Star-Lord is looting a temple?
- **a** Morag
- **b** Knowhere
- **c** Earth

2. A reformed villain has joined the Ravagers. Who is he?
- **a** Thanos
- **b** Kingpin
- **c** Ultron

3. What nickname does Korath give Thanos?
- **a** Captain Pacific
- **b** Captain Genocide
- **c** Captain Universe

4. What is the name of the cosmic dust that can heal a dying planet that the Ravagers are looking for?
- **a** The Seeds of Regeneration
- **b** The Cosmic Particles
- **c** The Embers of Genesis

5. Which character locked in the Collector's museum does T'Challa release?
a Howard the Duck
b Groot
c Iron Man

6. Whose crown does the Collector wear to confront T'Challa?
a Thor's
b Iron Man's
c Hela's

7. What nickname does Nebula call T'Challa?
a Baba
b Cha-Cha
c Star Prince

8. What does T'Challa unexpectedly find inside the Collector's museum?
a A Wakanda space craft
b Vibranium
c The Tesseract

EPISODE 3: WHAT IF... THE WORLD LOST ITS MIGHTIEST HEROES?

1. When he appears in the episode, what is Tony Stark eating?
a Chimichanga
b Rum cake
c A doughnut

2. Where is Thor's hammer discovered?
a   In New Mexico
b   In the Sahara
c   On a beach in Normandy

3. According to Coulson, what does Thor smell like?
a   The sea air
b   Lavender
c   Rosemary

4. What weapon does Loki use to attack S.H.I.E.L.D.?
a   The Tesseract
b   Mjolnir, Thor's hammer·
c   A sceptre

5. What is Coulson's password?
a   #hailhydra666
b   #excelsior2812
c   #Steve-Steve-Steve-I_heart-Steve-O-7-O-4

EPISODE 4: WHAT IF... DOCTOR STRANGE LOST HIS HEART INSTEAD OF HIS HANDS?

1. What dessert did Stephen Strange promise his girlfriend?
a   A rum baba
b   A peach melba
c   A crème brûlée

◢□□ **2.** What is the name of Stephen Strange's girlfriend?
  a   Dr. Christine Palmer
  b   Dr. Jane Foster
  c   Dr. Darcy Lewis

◢◢◢ **3.** What is the name of the artefact that Doctor Strange possesses?
  a   The Ark of the Covenant
  b   The Eye of Agamotto
  c   The Gem of Cyttorak

◢◢□ **4.** In his quest for knowledge, what is Doctor Strange looking for?
  a   The Hanging Gardens of Dormammu
  b   The Nightmare Colossus
  c   The Lost Library of Cagliostro

◢◢□ **5.** What is the name of the librarian for the books of Cagliostro?
  a   O'Brien
  b   O'Hara
  c   O'Bengh

◢□□ **6.** According to the book on time manipulation, what power is needed to break an Absolute Point – and therefore help Doctor Strange bring Christine Palmer back?
  a   The absorption of the power of other beings
  b   The sacrifice of innocent people
  c   Renouncing one's identity

261

EPISODE 5: WHAT IF... ZOMBIES?!

▰▱▱ **1.** When Hulk falls to Earth after running from Thanos, where does he crash?
- **a** Westview
- **b** The Sanctum Sanctorum
- **c** The Avengers Tower

▰▰▱ **2.** In this reality, who is the origin of the zombie outbreak?
- **a** Scott Lang (Ant-Man)
- **b** Hank Pym (the first Ant-Man)
- **c** Janet van Dyne (the first Wasp)

▰▰▱ **3.** Which zombified character turns Happy Hogan into a zombie?
- **a** Hawkeye
- **b** Wanda Maximoff
- **c** Captain America

▰▱▱ **4.** What item does Bucky Barnes get back while on the train to New Jersey?
- **a** Falcon's wings
- **b** Thor's hammer
- **c** Captain America's shield

▰▰▰ **5.** What can repel the zombies?
- **a** The Mind Stone that Vision carries
- **b** Hulk's gamma radiation
- **c** The magical aura of Doctor Strange's cape

▰▰▰ **6.** Where could the salvation of humanity be found?

a   On the dark side of the Moon

b   In Wakanda

c   In Sokovia

EPISODE 6: WHAT IF... KILLMONGER RESCUED TONY STARK?

▰▰▱ **1.** Who saves Tony Stark and is promoted as Stark Industries' new chief security officer?

a   Obadiah Stane

b   Lieutenant Erik Stevens

c   Happy Hogan

▰▰▱ **2.** What was the name of Killmonger's drone project?

a   Project Liberator

b   Project Freedom

c   Project Eliminator

▰▱▱ **3.** What element is needed to power Tony's and Killmonger's drones?

a   Uranium

b   Adamantium

c   Vibranium

◢◢◢ **4.** What type of weapon helps Killmonger defeat T'Challa?

   a   An ancient weapon

   b   A nuclear weapon

   c   A sonic weapon

◢◢◻ **5.** Who commands the Wakanda army?

   a   Ramonda

   b   T'Chaka

   c   Shuri

◢◢◻ **6.** Who tries to save Wakanda at the end of the episode?

   a   Steve Rogers and Bucky Barnes

   b   Shuri and Pepper Potts

   c   Groot and Rocket

EPISODE 7: WHAT IF... THOR WERE AN ONLY CHILD?

◢◢◻ **1.** In her absence, who does Frigga order to watch Thor?

   a   Lady Sif

   b   Loki

   c   Heimdall

◢◢◢ **2.** Who does Darcy marry in Las Vegas?

   a   Howard the Duck

   b   Drax

   c   The Grandmaster

3. In which city does Thor meet Loki, the leader of the Frost Giants?

a Rome
b Paris
c New York

4. Who does S.H.I.E.L.D. call upon to fight against Party Thor?

a Captain Marvel
b The Avengers
c Doctor Strange

5. Thor faces a villain who has retrieved the Infinity Stones. Who is it?

a Dormammu
b Thanos
c Ultron

6. When speaking to his mother, what excuse does Thor use when explaining why he is on Midgard?

a To save Loki
b For a cultural exchange study group
c To find Thanos

EPISODE 8: WHAT IF... ULTRON WON?

1. By whom is the nuclear apocalypse described in this episode brought about?

a Dormammu
b Hulk
c Ultron

2. Which body part does Hawkeye lose?

a Left leg

b Right arm

c Feet

3. After Earth, Ultron attacks other worlds. Where does he start?

a Asgard

b The Moon

c Midgard

4. What oath does The Watcher of the Multiverse take?

a To uphold the Sacred Timeline

b To not intervene

c To champion the innocent

5. Who is the program that can combat Ultron's code?

a JARVIS

b FRIDAY

c Zola

EPISODE 9: WHAT IF... THE WATCHER BROKE HIS OATH?

1. What is the name of the team of heroes chosen by The Watcher?

a The Interdimensional Avengers

b The Guardians of the Multiverse

c The Amazing Eight

2. What device does Gamora have to destroy the Infinity Stones?

a   The Infinity Crusher

b   The Infinity Destroyer

c   The Infinity Gauntlet

3. Who is the most powerful zombie summoned by Doctor Strange?

a   Hulk

b   Wanda Maximoff

c   Thor

4. What are the three elements that The Watcher says creates a prism of endless possibilty?

a   Power, soul and spirit

b   Time, space and reality

c   Love, patience and reason

5. Who defeats Ultron?

a   Arnim Zola

b   Natasha Romanoff

c   Doctor Strange

6. Who takes over the Infinity Stones after Ultron is defeated?

a   Doctor Strange

b   Captain Carter

c   Erik Killmonger

HAWKEYE

EPISODE 1: NEVER MEET YOUR HEROES

1. Clint and his family go to see a musical in New York. What is its title?
  a *Captain America: The Musical*
  b *Avengers: The Musical*
  c *Rogers: The Musical*

2. How many tries does it take Kate to ring the bell?
  a One
  b Two
  c Five

3. What is the name of the group that Clint and Kate are fighting?
  a The Jogging Gang
  b The Tracksuit Mafia
  c The Sweatshirt Crew

4. At the time of the Chitauri invasion, her mother suggests that Kate play a game. Which one?
  a Checkers
  b Chess
  c Bridge

5. To ring the old school bell, what does Kate weight her arrow with?
- **a** A golf ball
- **b** A baseball
- **c** A tennis ball

6. Which Avenger featured in the musical was not actually present in the battle that is depicted?
- **a** Ant-Man
- **b** Spider-Man
- **c** Black Panther

7. Which intriguing graffiti does Clint see in the bathroom?
- **a** 'Odin was right'
- **b** 'Loki was right'
- **c** 'Thanos was right'

8. At what age did Kate become a black belt in martial arts?
- **a** 7 years old
- **b** 15 years old
- **c** 22 years old

9. What is the special feature of the blade of Ronin's sword that is being auctioned?

a   It is a laser
b   It is retractable
c   It is electric

10. Where was Ronin's sword found before being listed for auction?

a   In the rubble of the Avengers Compound
b   On Asgard
c   In Hong Kong

11. What does the Tracksuit Mafia want to get back when they attack the auction?

a   A sword
b   A painting
c   A watch

EPISODE 2: HIDE AND SEEK

1. At what age did Kate start martial arts?

a   5 years old
b   10 years old
c   15 years old

2. Kate's apartment is located on top of what kind of store?
a   A comic book store
b   A pizzeria
c   A grocery store

3. How old is Kate Bishop during the events described in the series?
a   18 years old
b   20 years old
c   22 years old

4. Where do Kate and Clint hide for safety?
a   Kate's aunt's apartment
b   A hotel room
c   Kate's parents' home

5. Where does Clint retrieve the Ronin costume?
a   At a cosplay contest
b   At a live-action role-playing game
c   At a ritual

6. In which sport does Kate challenge Jack Duquesne to a duel to test his skills?
a   Polo
b   Squash
c   Fencing

EPISODE 3: ECHOES

1. What is the sport that Maya learned as a child?
- **a**   Kung-Fu
- **b**   Karate
- **c**   Judo

2. When the Tracksuit Mafia captures Clint Barton, he is tied up to:
- **a**   A dragon
- **b**   A unicorn
- **c**   A panther

3. What does Kate give a member of the Tracksuit Mafia advice about?
- **a**   Renting a new apartment
- **b**   Finding a new job
- **c**   An argument with his girlfriend

4. Clint says that Ronin has been killed by:
- **a**   Thanos
- **b**   Crossbones
- **c**   Black Widow

5. The Tracksuit Mafia holds Clint and Kate captive in:
a An abandoned toy store
b A deserted circus
c An old video store

6. During his fight against the Tracksuit Mafia, Clint hides in:
a A sofa bed
b A ball pit
c A cabinet

7. In her room, young Kate has a giant stuffed animal. What is its shape?
a Dolphin
b Rhinoceros
c Giraffe

8. The putty arrow explodes into a coloured paste. What is the paste colour?
a Green
b Purple
c Pink

9. Which type of arrow did Kate mention was completely useless?
a Balloon
b Pym
c Plunger

10. Who does Maya want to get revenge on?
a   Hawkeye
b   Ronin
c   Thor

EPISODE 4: PARTNERS, AM I RIGHT?

1. What does Jack Duquesne call Clint when he first meets him?
a   Purple Arrow
b   Archer
c   Robin Hood

2. What is Kate's mother's first name?
a   Laura
b   Natasha
c   Eleanor

3. What animal is featured on the Christmas jumper Kate gives Clint?
a   A cat
b   A rabbit
c   A horse

4. Kate praises a new model of gadget arrow. Which one is it?
a   The boxing glove arrow
b   The laser arrow
c   The boomerang arrow

5. What does Kate bring to the apartment Clint is staying in?

a   A pizza and a new suit

b   A pizza and Christmas cheer

c   Hot dogs and Pizza Dog

6. What does Clint use to show Kate a trick that knocks someone unconscious?

a   A coin

b   A playing card

c   A stuffed animal

7. Who is the masked assassin who confronts Clint on a roof?

a   Loki

b   Black Widow

c   The Winter Soldier

8. What is the name of Jack Duquesne's shell company?

a   West LTD

b   Sloan LTD

c   Conrad LTD

9. What object does Kate draw on while at the apartment to discuss a plan with Clint?

a   A dry erase board

b   The wall

c   A movie poster

10. Whose apartment does Kate break into to investigate?

a   Kazi's apartment

b   Maya's apartment

c   Jack's apartment

EPISODE 5: RONIN

1. What trick does Grills teach Pizza Dog?

a   To fetch

b   To sing

c   To dance

2. What did Yelena prepare while she was waiting for Kate at her house?

a   Borscht

b   Macaroni and cheese

c   Hamburgers

3. Why is Yelena in New York?

a   To kill Kingpin

b   To kill Kate Bishop

c   To kill Clint Barton

4. What does Kate have a picture of on top of her bed?
- **a** Captain America
- **b** A purple feather
- **c** A clock

5. Where does the meeting between Maya and Ronin take place?
- **a** At a used car dealer
- **b** At a Christmas tree shop
- **c** At an Avengers souvenir shop

6. Who hired Yelena?
- **a** Jack Duquesne
- **b** Wilson Fisk
- **c** Eleanor Bishop

EPISODE 6: SO THIS IS CHRISTMAS ?

1. Where does Kate follow Yelena to at the Christmas party?
- **a** Into a lift
- **b** Into the kitchen
- **c** Outside the plaza

2. What is on the top of Kingpin's cane?
- **a** A diamond
- **b** An eagle's head
- **c** A skull

3. Where does the final Christmas party take place?
a   At Rockefeller Plaza
b   In Central Park
c   In the Empire State Building

4. Who helps Kate defeat some of the Tracksuit Mafia?
a   Eleanor Bishop
b   Jack Duquesne
c   Yelena

5. When Clint falls into the giant tree in Rockefeller Plaza, who does he run into?
a   Redwing
b   A member of the Tracksuit Mafia
c   An owl

6. Where does Kate fight off Kingpin?
a   In a toy store
b   In a pizzeria
c   On the ice rink

7. What company name appears on the Tracksuit Mafia's truck?
a   Trust A Bro
b   X-Con Security Consultants
c   Roxxon

8. In front of Kingpin, what does Kate use to fire the 'too dangerous' arrow?
- **a** A quarter
- **b** A cufflink
- **c** A credit card

9. Clint is hard of hearing in:
- **a** His right ear
- **b** His left ear
- **c** Both ears

MOON KNIGHT

EPISODE 1: THE GOLDFISH PROBLEM

1. What does Steven surround his bed with every night?

a Sand

b Toy bricks

c Nails

2. What is Steven's job at the museum?

a Tour guide

b Security guard

c Gift shop cashier

3. What does Steven's Staying Awake app not suggest as a way of keeping him from falling asleep?

a Solving a puzzle

b Doing squats

c Reading a book

4. What is tattooed on Arthur's forearm?

a An eye

b A feather

c A set of scales

5. What kind of van does Steven use to escape Arthur's men in the Alps?

a An ice cream van

b A cupcake van

c A hot dog van

6. What food does Steven order on his failed date?

a   Steak

b   Pizza

c   Fish and chips

7. What type of animal videos is J.B., the museum's security guard, watching on his phone?

a   Cats

b   Otters

c   Sharks

8. In which room does Steven hide when pursued by the mysterious creature in the museum?

a   Security booth

b   Gift shop

c   Toilets

EPISODE 2: SUMMON THE SUIT

1. What is Steven sacked from the museum for?

a   Theft

b   Vandalism

c   Arson

2. What number is Marc's storage locker?

a   043

b   102

c   68

3. Which Egyptian god is Marc Spector the avatar of?

a   Khonshu

b   Hathor

c   Ammit

4. Who rescues Steven as he flees the storage unit?

a   Arthur

b   Anton

c   Layla

5. What kind of food does Arthur offer Steven?

a   Macaroni cheese

b   Lentil soup

c   Tomato salad

6. What does Layla throw at the creature to distract it from attacking Steven?

a   A glass bottle

b   A stone

c   Her shoe

▰▰▰ 7. What number is the bus that Steven crashes into while fighting the creature?

a 1
b 17
c 25

▰▱▱ 8. Who does Khonshu threaten to make his next avatar?

a Layla
b Steven
c Arthur

EPISODE 3: THE FRIENDLY TYPE

▰▰▱ 1. How long has it been since Layla was last home?

a Six months
b One year
c Ten years

▰▰▱ 2. Where does Steven try to get a taxi to in Cairo?

a Ammit's tomb
b The airport
c A hotel

3. 'You're getting desperate, old bird.' Who says this about Khonshu?

a   Arthur

b   Steven

c   Marc

4. Who is Yatzil an avatar of?

a   Hathor

b   Ammit

c   Horus

5. 'I hope you like attention.' Who greets Steven with these words?

a   Arthur

b   Yatzil

c   Layla

6. What does Layla tell Anton Marc is doing when he goes to talk to Steven?

a   Working things out

b   Praying

c   Using the bathroom

7. What sport does Anton engage in?

a   Boxing

b   Jousting

c   Fencing

■■□ **8.** What's wrong with the star map?
- **a** Half of it is missing
- **b** It's stained with coffee
- **c** It's 2,000 years out of date

EPISODE 4: THE TOMB

■■□ **1.** What does Layla use to ward off the van attacking her and Steven in the desert?
- **a** A baton
- **b** A flare
- **c** A baseball bat

■■■ **2.** How does Steven first react to Layla trying to kiss him?
- **a** He tells her that Marc is trying to protect her
- **b** He screams and jumps back
- **c** He laughs

■□□ **3.** What was Layla's father's profession?
- **a** Archaeologist
- **b** Taxi driver
- **c** English professor

■■□ **4.** What is Ammit's tomb in the shape of?
- **a** A cat's skull
- **b** A set of scales
- **c** The Eye of Horus

5. Which pharaoh's sarcophagus does Steven discover?

a   Cleopatra

b   Tutankhamun

c   Alexander the Great

6. What colour was the scarf worn by Layla's father?

a   Jade green

b   Fuschia

c   Lilac

7. Where was Ammit's ushabti?

a   Alexander's throat

b   Alexander's hand

c   Alexander's eye socket

8. What is the name of the movie featuring Dr. Steven Grant that Marc watches in the psychiatric hospital?

a   *Tomb Explorer*

b   *Tomb Quester*

c   *Tomb Buster*

EPISODE 5: ASYLUM

1. Which city is Putnam Medical Facility allegedly in?

a   Chicago, IL

b   New York City, NY

c   Dallas, TX

▰▰▰ **2.** What is the hippo-headed goddess Taweret god of?

a   The dead

b   Women and children

c   Travellers

▰▰▱ **3.** In his memory, what is Steven's brother drawing a picture of?

a   A one-finned fish

b   The Eye of Horus

c   A bird-headed man

▰▱▱ **4.** How did Steven's brother Randall die?

a   He was hit by a car

b   He accidentally ate rat poison

c   He drowned in a cave

▰▰▱ **5.** Whose gate does Taweret say is the only path back to the living world?

a   Osiris'

b   Horus'

c   Ra's

▰▰▰ **6.** When young Marc first creates Steven, what does he pick up from his bedroom floor?

a   An action figure

b   Coloured pens

c   A lunch box

▰▱▱ **7. True or false?** Steven and Marc's mother is alive.

▰▰▱ **8.** Who is dragged into the Duat?
  a   Marc
  b   Steven
  c   Jake

EPISODE 6: GODS AND MONSTERS

▰▰▰ **1.** How many of the Egyptian police officers that Harrow 'judges' survive?
  a   0
  b   1
  c   10

▰▱▱ **2.** Ammit has the head of which creature?
  a   Crocodile
  b   Jackal
  c   Lion

▰▱▱ **3.** Who frees Khonshu from his ushabti?
  a   Marc
  b   Harrow
  c   Layla

4. How does Marc describe the Field of Reeds when he first sees it?

a   Beautiful

b   Quiet

c   Boring

5. What does Marc call the 'only real superpower I ever had'?

a   His ability to be Steven

b   His ability to evade death

c   His love for Layla

6. Who does Layla become an avatar of?

a   Ammit

b   Taweret

c   Khonshu

7. What is Marc talking about when he tells Khonshu to 'do it yourself'?

a   Killing Harrow

b   Fighting Osiris

c   Binding the other gods in an ushabti

8. What is the number plate of the limo driven by Jake Lockley in the mid-credits scene?

a   M N K N T

b   K N S H U

c   S P K T R

ANSWERS

IRON MAN

1. A
2. B
3. A
4. C
5. C
6. B
7. A
8. B
9. A
10. A
11. B
12. A
13. A
14. C
15. B
16. A
17. False, it's the MARK III
18. C
19. A
20. B
21. C
22. A
23. C
24. A
25. B

THE INCREDIBLE HULK

1. B
2. A
3. B
4. C
5. A
6. B
7. C
8. A
9. B
10. A
11. C
12. B
13. B
14. A
15. B
16. A
17. C
18. C
19. A
20. B
21. A
22. C
23. B
24. A
25. B

IRON MAN 2

1. C
2. A

3.	C
4.	B
5.	C
6.	C
7.	A
8.	B
9.	A
10.	C
11.	A
12.	B
13.	C
14.	C
15.	A
16.	C
17.	B
18.	C
19.	A
20.	B
21.	C
22.	A
23.	B
24.	B
25.	A

THOR

1.	C
2.	A
3.	B
4.	B
5.	A

6.	C
7.	B
8.	C
9.	A
10.	B
11.	The right eye
12.	A
13.	C
14.	B and D, Dr. Erik Selvig speaks these words, but they were whispered to him by Loki
15.	A
16.	B
17.	A
18.	C
19.	B
20.	C
21.	A
22.	C
23.	B
24.	A
25.	C

CAPTAIN AMERICA: THE FIRST AVENGER

1. B
2. A
3. C
4. A
5. C and D
6. A
7. B
8. C
9. B
10. C
11. A
12. C
13. A
14. B
15. C
16. C
17. A
18. B
19. A
20. C
21. B
22. A
23. C
24. A
25. B
26. C
27. A

28. B
29. A
30. C

MARVEL'S THE AVENGERS

1. B; Captain America, Iron Man, Hulk, Thor, Black Widow, Hawkeye
2. A
3. A
4. C
5. B
6. C
7. A
8. C
9. B
10. B
11. A
12. C
13. A
14. B
15. C
16. A
17. B
18. B
19. A

20.	C		14.	B
21.	B		15.	B
22.	A		16.	C
23.	A		17.	A
24.	C		18.	B
25.	B		19.	A
26.	B		20.	C
27.	A		21.	A
28.	B		22.	B
29.	A		23.	B
30.	C		24.	A
31.	A		25.	C
32.	C			
33.	B			
34.	A			
35.	A			

THOR: THE DARK WORLD

			1.	A
			2.	C
			3.	B

IRON MAN 3

1.	C		4.	B
2.	A		5.	A
3.	B		6.	C
4.	B		7.	A
5.	A		8.	C
6.	A		9.	B
7.	C		10.	A
8.	B		11.	C
9.	B		12.	B
10.	A		13.	C
11.	A		14.	A
12.	C		15.	B
13.	A		16.	A

17.	C		17.	B
18.	A		18.	B
19.	B		19.	A
20.	A		20.	A
21.	B		21.	B
22.	C		22.	C
23.	A		23.	C
24.	C		24.	A
25.	B		25.	B
			26.	C

CAPTAIN AMERICA: THE WINTER SOLDIER

27.	A
28.	B
29.	C
30.	A

1. B
2. A
3. B
4. C
5. A
6. B
7. A
8. C
9. C
10. A
11. B
12. A
13. C
14. A
15. B
16. C

GUARDIANS OF THE GALAXY

1. A
2. C
3. C
4. A
5. B
6. C
7. A
8. B
9. C
10. C
11. B
12. C
13. A

14.	B
15.	C
16.	A
17.	A
18.	C
19.	A
20.	B
21.	C
22.	A
23.	A
24.	B
25.	B
26.	B
27.	C
28.	B
29.	A
30.	A
31.	C
32.	B
33.	A
34.	A
35.	C

AVENGERS: AGE OF ULTRON

1.	A
2.	B
3.	A
4.	C
5.	A

6.	B
7.	C
8.	A
9.	B
10.	C
11.	A
12.	C
13.	B
14.	C
15.	A
16.	A
17.	B
18.	B
19.	A
20.	C
21.	B
22.	A
23.	B
24.	A
25.	C
26.	A
27.	C
28.	B
29.	A
30.	B

ANT-MAN

1.	B
2.	A
3.	A
4.	C

5. Peggy Carter,
   Howard Stark
   or Mitchell
   Carson
6. B
7. A
8. C
9. B
10. A
11. C
12. B
13. B
14. A
15. B
16. A
17. C
18. B
19. C
20. C
21. B
22. C
23. B
24. A
25. B

CAPTAIN AMERICA: CIVIL WAR

1. A

2. C
3. A
4. B
5. B
6. B
7. A
8. C
9. B
10. B
11. A
12. B
13. A
14. C
15. B
16. True
17. C
18. B
19. C
20. A
21. A
22. C
23. B
24. C
25. C
26. B
27. B
28. A
29. A
30. C

ANSWERS

DOCTOR STRANGE

1. A
2. C
3. B
4. B
5. A
6. C
7. A
8. B
9. B
10. A
11. A
12. C
13. A
14. C
15. B
16. C
17. A
18. C
19. B
20. C
21. A
22. A
23. C
24. B
25. B

GUARDIANS OF THE GALAXY VOL. 2

1. B
2. A
3. True
4. C
5. B
6. C
7. B
8. C
9. A
10. C
11. A
12. B
13. C
14. C
15. A
16. B
17. A
18. B
19. C
20. A
21. A
22. B
23. A
24. B
25. A

THOR: RAGNAROK

1. C
2. B
3. C
4. A
5. B
6. A
7. C
8. A
9. B
10. B
11. A
12. C
13. B
14. A
15. C
16. B
17. A
18. C
19. C
20. B
21. A
22. B
23. B
24. C
25. C

BLACK PANTHER

1. B
2. A
3. C
4. B
5. C
6. A
7. B
8. A
9. C
10. C
11. B
12. C
13. B
14. A
15. A
16. C
17. B
18. C
19. A
20. C
21. C
22. A
23. C
24. B
25. A
26. A
27. C
28. B
29. A

30.	B
31.	B
32.	A
33.	C
34.	A
35.	B

AVENGERS: INFINITY WAR

1.	B
2.	C
3.	B
4.	A
5.	A
6.	C
7.	B
8.	A
9.	C
10.	B
11.	C
12.	A
13.	A
14.	C
15.	A
16.	B
17.	B
18.	A
19.	C
20.	A
21.	B
22.	B

23.	Captain America, Iron Man, Thor, Hulk, Black Widow, War Machine. We don't know what happened to Hawkeye, Ant-Man and The Wasp.
24.	C
25.	A
26.	B
27.	B
28.	A
29.	B
30.	C
31.	B
32.	A
33.	B
34.	A
35.	C
36.	C
37.	B
38.	C
39.	B
40.	A
41.	B
42.	A
43.	C

44.	A
45.	C

ANT-MAN AND THE WASP

1.	B
2.	C
3.	B
4.	C
5.	A
6.	A
7.	C
8.	B
9.	A
10.	C
11.	A
12.	A
13.	C
14.	A
15.	B
16.	C
17.	A
18.	B
19.	C
20.	A
21.	A
22.	B
23.	A
24.	C
25.	A

CAPTAIN MARVEL

1.	B
2.	A
3.	C
4.	B
5.	A
6.	A
7.	C
8.	A
9.	A
10.	B
11.	B
12.	A
13.	C
14.	B
15.	A
16.	C
17.	A
18.	B
19.	A
20.	True
21.	B
22.	C
23.	A
24.	B
25.	C
26.	B
27.	A
28.	B
29.	C
30.	A

AVENGERS: ENDGAME

1. C
2. A
3. C
4. B
5. False
6. A
7. C
8. A
9. B
10. A
11. C
12. B
13. A
14. C
15. A
16. C
17. B
18. A
19. C
20. C
21. A
22. A
23. B
24. B
25. A
26. C
27. B
28. A
29. A

30. C

BLACK WIDOW

1. C
2. A
3. A
4. B
5. C
6. C
7. A
8. C
9. B
10. A
11. C
12. A
13. B
14. A
15. C
16. C
17. B
18. B
19. C
20. B
21. A
22. C
23. C
24. B
25. A
26. B
27. A
28. C

29. A
30. B

SHANG-CHI AND THE LEGEND OF THE TEN RINGS

1. B
2. A
3. B
4. C
5. C
6. A
7. B
8. B
9. A
10. C
11. B
12. B
13. A
14. C
15. B
16. A
17. C
18. A
19. C
20. False
21. B
22. C
23. C
24. B

25. A
26. B
27. A
28. False
29. B
30. A

ETERNALS

1. C
2. A
3. C
4. A
5. B
6. A
7. B
8. C
9. B
10. A
11. C
12. A
13. B
14. B
15. C
16. A
17. C
18. B
19. C
20. False
21. A
22. C

23. A	19. C
24. C	20. B
25. B	21. A
26. A	22. C
27. C	23. A
28. A	24. True
29. B	25. C
30. A	

DOCTOR STRANGE IN THE MULTIVERSE OF MADNESS

1. C
2. A
3. A
4. B
5. C
6. A
7. C
8. A
9. B
10. A
11. C
12. B
13. C
14. B
15. B
16. A
17. C
18. B

WANDAVISION

EPISODE 1: FILMED BEFORE A LIVE STUDIO AUDIENCE

1. B
2. A
3. A
4. C
5. A
6. A

EPISODE 2: DON'T TOUCH THAT DIAL

1. A
2. C
3. C
4. B
5. A
6. B

EPISODE 3: NOW IN COLOR

1. B
2. C
3. B
4. C
5. A
6. C

EPISODE 4: WE INTERRUPT THIS PROGRAM

1. A
2. A
3. B
4. A
5. C
6. B
7. A

EPISODE 5: ON A VERY SPECIAL EPISODE...

1. C
2. A
3. B
4. A

EPISODE 6: ALL-NEW HALLOWEEN SPOOKTACULAR!

1. B
2. A
3. C
4. B

EPISODE 7: BREAKING THE FOURTH WALL

1. A
2. C
3. C
4. A
5. C

EPISODE 8: PREVIOUSLY ON

1. B
2. B
3. C

EPISODE 9: THE SERIES FINALE

1. C
2. B
3. A
4. C

LOKI

EPISODE 1: GLORIOUS PURPOSE

1. A
2. C
3. B
4. A
5. B
6. A

EPISODE 2: THE VARIANT

1. A
2. C
3. B
4. A
5. C

EPISODE 3: LAMENTIS

1. A
2. C
3. C
4. B
5. A
6. B
7. A
8. C

EPISODE 4: THE NEXUS EVENT

1. B
2. C
3. B
4. C
5. A
6. C
7. B
8. B
9. C

EPISODE 5: JOURNEY INTO MYSTERY

1. C
2. A
3. A
4. C
5. B
6. A
7. C
8. A
9. C

EPISODE 6: FOR ALL TIME. ALWAYS.

1. B
2. A
3. C

4. C
5. B
6. B

THE FALCON AND THE WINTER SOLDIER

EPISODE 1: NEW WORLD ORDER

1. C
2. A
3. C
4. B
5. C
6. C
7. A
8. C
9. C

EPISODE 2: THE STAR-SPANGLED MAN

1. C
2. B
3. C
4. A
5. A
6. A

7. C
8. B

EPISODE 3: POWER BROKER

1. C
2. A
3. B
4. B
5. B

EPISODE 4: THE WHOLE WORLD IS WATCHING

1. A
2. A
3. C
4. C
5. A
6. C
7. C

EPISODE 5: TRUTH

1. C
2. A
3. B
4. B
5. A
6. A
7. B

EPISODE 6: ONE WORLD, ONE PEOPLE

1. A
2. C
3. A
4. A
5. A
6. C

MARVEL WHAT IF...?

EPISODE 1: WHAT IF... CAPTAIN CARTER WERE THE FIRST AVENGER?

1. A
2. A
3. B
4. A
5. C
6. A
7. B
8. B
9. A

EPISODE 2: WHAT IF... T'CHALLA BECAME A STAR-LORD?

1. A
2. A
3. B
4. C
5. A
6. C
7. B
8. A

EPISODE 3: WHAT IF... THE WORLD LOST ITS MIGHTIEST HEROES?

1. C
2. A
3. B
4. A
5. C

ANSWERS

**EPISODE 4:
WHAT IF...
DOCTOR
STRANGE LOST
HIS HEART
INSTEAD OF HIS
HANDS?**

1. C
2. A
3. B
4. C
5. C
6. A

**EPISODE 5:
WHAT IF...
ZOMBIES?!**

1. B
2. C
3. A
4. C
5. A
6. B

**EPISODE 6:
WHAT IF...
KILLMONGER
RESCUED TONY
STARK?**

1. B
2. A
3. C
4. C
5. A
6. B

**EPISODE 7:
WHAT IF... THOR
WERE AN ONLY
CHILD?**

1. C
2. A
3. B
4. A
5. C
6. B

**EPISODE 8:
WHAT IF...
ULTRON WON?**

1. C
2. B
3. A
4. B
5. C

EPISODE 9: WHAT IF... THE WATCHER BROKE HIS OATH?

1. B
2. A
3. B
4. B
5. A
6. C

HAWKEYE

EPISODE 1: NEVER MEET YOUR HEROES

1. C
2. B
3. B
4. A
5. C
6. A
7. C
8. B
9. B
10. A
11. C

EPISODE 2: HIDE AND SEEK

1. A
2. B
3. C
4. A
5. B
6. C

EPISODE 3: ECHOES

1. B
2. B
3. C
4. C
5. A
6. B
7. C
8. B
9. C
10. B

EPISODE 4: PARTNERS, AM I RIGHT?

1. B
2. C
3. A
4. C
5. B
6. A

7. B
8. B
9. C
10. B

EPISODE 5:
RONIN

1. C
2. B
3. C
4. B
5. A
6. C

EPISODE 6:
SO THIS IS
CHRISTMAS?

1. A
2. A
3. A
4. B
5. C
6. A
7. A
8. B
9. B

MOON KNIGHT

EPISODE 1:
THE GOLDFISH
PROBLEM

1. A
2. C
3. B
4. C
5. B
6. A
7. B
8. C

EPISODE 2:
SUMMON THE
SUIT

1. B
2. A
3. A
4. C
5. B
6. A
7. C
8. A

EPISODE 3:
THE FRIENDLY
TYPE

1. C
2. B
3. A
4. A
5. C
6. B
7. B
8. C

EPISODE 4:
THE TOMB

1. B
2. A
3. A
4. C
5. C
6. B
7. A
8. C

EPISODE 5:
ASYLUM

1. A
2. B
3. A
4. C
5. A

6. B
7. False
8. B

EPISODE 6:
GODS AND
MONSTERS

1. B
2. A
3. C
4. B
5. A
6. B
7. A
8. C

NOTES

NOTES

NOTES